Radiation

What It Is, How It Affects Us And What We Can Do About It

by John H. Davidson M.A. Cantab

SAFFRON WALDEN
THE C.W. DANIEL COMPANY LIMITED

First published in Great Britain in 1986
by The C.W. Daniel Company Limited
1 Church Path, Saffron Walden,
Essex CB10 1JP, England

ISBN 0 85207 180 9

Design and Production in association
with Book Production Consultants, Cambridge
Typeset by Cambridge Photosetting Services in Bembo
Printed and bound in Great Britain by
Heffers Printers Limited

Dedication

To all the living creatures on our planet.
The next fifty years will be crucial.
I hope we get it right.

Contents

FOREWORD – *Farida Davidson*   7

INTRODUCTION   11

CHAPTER 1 – **Energy And Radiation:** *Energy and the Atom;
Radiation; Nuclear Radiation and Fall-Out;
Radioactive Isotopes; Radioactive Half-Life; The
Chernobyl Cocktail; Safety Levels; Natural
Background Levels; Artificial Levels of Radiation;
Radon Gas; Danger Units – A Way of Combining
the Safe Limits of Exposure to Toxins, Mutagens
and Carcinogens, also Relating them to our
Lifestyle; A Confusion of Facts*   13

CHAPTER 2 – **Biological Effects of Radiation:** *Units of
Radiation Measurement; Metabolism and the
Effects of Radiation; Genetic Problems and
Radiation; Target Organs; Short Term Biological
Symptoms and Lethal Doses*   37

CHAPTER 3 – **Radiation, Subtle Energy and
Electromagnetism:**
*Subtle Energy; Subtle Energy Terminology;
Bodily Polarities; What Effects Subtle Energy
Harmony and Polarity?; Vibrational and
Electromagnetic Pollution; Bio-Entrainment*   46

CHAPTER 4 – **Natural Protection from Radiation:** *Avoiding
Radiation; Anti-Oxidants; The Immune System;
Iodine and Kelp; Heavy Metal Blockers and
Purifiers; Chinese Herbs of Power: Ginseng Panax,
Eleutherococcus, Tang Kwei, Astragulus,
Ligusticum; Bee Products: Honey, Royal Jelly,
Propolis and Pollen; The Macrobiotic Approach –
The Diet That Saved Thousands; Miscellaneous
Special Nutrients; Exercise; Mental and Emotional
Attitudes; A Cleansing and Drawing Programme;
Homoeopathy and Radiation; Bach Flower
Remedies; Subtle Energy Balancing – Pulsors;
In Conclusion*   59

EPILOGUE   86

BIBLIOGRAPHY AND FURTHER READING   90

FURTHER INFORMATION   93

Acknowledgements

This book has been written quite rapidly in response to demand and I would like to thank all those who have given so much of their time and knowledge in helping to put it together.

Monica Bryant was the catalyst who turned a background of thoughts into the crystallization of writing it all down in book form. Simon Martin, Franklyn Sills, Celia Wright, Anthony Scott-Morley, Sue Evans, Christopher Seeback, Nigel Bell and the Dr. Bach Centre all provided valuable information. My wife, Farida, provided further insights; Roger Savage kindly performed some necessary editing; Sheila Clarke typed it into my word processor and my publisher, Ian Miller, was his usual enthusiastic self, being ready to print it after only a brief discussion of the idea.

I am grateful, too, for all the research performed by so many people, especially on the healing side, whose work I have drawn upon as source material for this book. References are given in the 'Bibliography and Further Reading Section', at the rear.

Foreword

by Farida Davidson

Farida Davidson is director and founder of the School of Natural Medicine and the British School of Iridology. Well-loved and respected amongst the healing professions in England, she is a teacher, writer, herbalist, iridologist and practitioner of Natural Medicine, with practices in both Cambridge and London. She is also the wife of the author and has to bear some of the responsibility for re-educating his Cambridge-trained outlook.

Just as human beings carry the seeds of their own degeneration, so too do the different cultures and ages nurture the seeds of their own destruction.

Ancient Rome was brought to her knees because of malaria which insidiously weakened the Romans of all classes until they were overcome by barbarians, after centuries of dominance in the ancient world. The malaria was the result of mosquito-breeding swamps which came into being after the farmers in the Italian countryside gave up their simple hardworking lives to flock to Rome where they lived off the state and enjoyed the cruel spectacles in the Colliseum. When the Romans were laid to seige, distant food supplies were cut off and defeat inevitable.

Similarly, the isolation of European Royal houses may have given them the opportunity to create personal 'heavens' and live amidst riches, but it inexorably led to revolution, beheading and the loss of royal family lines.

Those more peaceful civilizations which endured for long periods of time without destroying themselves, or subduing others, eventually had to face destruction from outside invaders, or like the Hawaiians and North American Indians, fell prey to white man's diseases to which they had no defence.

Things can only go so far before there is a backlash in the often inexplicable ebb and flow of history.

Events at Chernobyl in the spring of 1986 have stimulated many of us to take a look at what is happening with atomic power and to reassess priorities. If we try to harness this vast power, will it not turn against us and destroy us? Life is so fragile. Do you not feel how easy it would be for mankind to suffer severe devastation in the face of such power?

Many of the diseases of our time are caused by our desire for material comfort, ease and wealth. The chemicals and materials that create the objects of which our dreams are made pollute our land, sea and air, rob our earth and ruin our forests. As if this were not enough, the increase of industrialization and the search for even more powerful weapons to protect us from each other makes us hungry for further raw materials and power that threatens life itself. We have harnessed and controlled nuclear power most inadequately and we have no defence against it.

How do we protect our bodies against destructive chemicals and energy? It is our lymphatic system which bears the brunt of the invasion of microbes, viruses and pollutants of many kinds. But, our lymphatic and immune systems are already overburdened by dealing with day-to-day pollutants, additives and exhaust fumes and weakened further by suppressive drugs.

What is our defence in a much larger sense against those destructive forces that threaten not only personal life, but the collective life of communities, cities, countries and the world?

While this book attempts to look at what we can do, and at the types of people who survived the Nagasaki holocaust, this is not enough. We have to go deeper into our very heart and soul and ask ourselves what we personally are contributing to this destructive force which has taken up residence in our world. We have created it from within ourselves and out of our devices. Can we undo what we have created? Can we as individuals ever begin to influence the governmental and business politics which have created these unsafe nuclear installations? There has been no lack of marches, camp-outs, picketing, letters and resistance against nuclear power in this country and yet nothing has changed. Is the individual helpless before political policies, such as the forces that created World Wars I and II? Is the urge for self-destruction so strong in all of us that it must inevitably manifest at regular intervals and create devastation and the most violent harm to human life?

Then again, certain people seem to withstand radiation and pollution better than others. It is important to find out why. We need all the keys we can find to unravel our own self-created knot.

Nuclear power has the potential to threaten life as we know it. How can we defend ourselves against it? What can we do to ensure that what is being used is handled safely and wisely? These questions need to be answered within each of us.

We can strengthen our immune system and protective biochemistry by purifying our bodies and living on foods which provide optimum nutrition. We can look at all the facts in this book as regards those who survived radiation in Japan and see how we can adjust the chemistry of our body to be able to resist radiation and pollution. But what we contribute to our community and global conscience is up to the individual. In such an issue as this you wouldn't want to look back and mourn that which might have been. At the present time it is not too late. Please don't wait until it is.

Farida Davidson M.H., N.D., F.B.R.I.
Cambridge, May 1986

Introduction

With the advent of the Chernobyl nuclear accident has come a more widespread desire for an awareness of what radiation is and how it effects us, biologically. After this incident, the nuclear industry cannot and should not remain the same. It must not be simply swept under the carpet in the hope that a similar disaster will not re-occur.

Because of my involvement and research into the effects of electromagnetic energies on life, I have received a number of telephone calls over the last couple of weeks from various friends and associates, which finally crystallized in the writing of this short book. My more complete study of this and allied subjects is contained in the book *Subtle Energy*, due for publication in 1986. These pages are a more specific 'what it is', 'how it affects us' and 'what to do about it.'

Nuclear power is a reflection of man at a crossroads. It stems from two aspects of our present nature and condition. Firstly, a beginning in our understanding of energy structure in the cosmos and secondly, our un-subtle, destructive and selfish approach to life on our planet.

Everything *is* energy, at whatever level you examine it – even our thoughts and emotions. And deep within this lies our consciousness, also energy, but highly refined in form and a drop of the Universal. At the gross physical level of crystallized energy patterns or matter, energy transformations are cumbersome and conducted with little real knowledge and hence involve danger. But man is an adventurer, he cannot help it, so we have our nuclear power plants, as well as so many other artifacts from which we can accidentally die – aeroplanes, motor cars, chemicals, electricity – in fact, more or less everything! We are indeed very clumsy and ignorant children!

But man *will* advance in knowledge, selflessness and subtlety. Then, perhaps, we will find easier ways of transforming the energy inherent in matter for our useful purposes, without the threat of global disaster. In the meantime, we have given ourselves a headache, so let us start at the beginning. We need first to understand the problem before we can do something about it.

John H. Davidson M.A. Cantab.
Cambridge, May 1986

CHAPTER I

Energy and Radiation

Energy and the Atom

All of the apparently solid, liquid or gaseous matter that we perceive is no more than a vibrating cosmic dance of energy. Starting from without and moving inwards, we observe or perceive matter through our senses in three dimensional form, structure, density, colour and sound. Its density makes it solid, liquid or gaseous and the movement of its atoms and molecules also gives rise to the sensations of heat or cold. Its interaction with the area of the electromagnetic spectrum we know of as light gives it colour, perceived through the eyes. Its ability to resonate and vibrate permits the formation of airborne wave forms, interpreted by our ears as sound. We also take cognisance of certain molecular relationships and structures through our organs of taste and smell. Some moths are so sensitive in this respect that they are aware of only one molecule of a pheromone (sex-chemical) emmitted by a female over thirty miles away. Of all the states, conditions and relationships in matter, our senses filter out only a tiny fraction of the available data, presenting it to us as our 'objective reality'.

Taking a step inwards, we find that matter is composed of molecules – some large, some small. Each molecule is composed of atoms. Each atom, until the advent of modern physics, was considered to consist of a nucleus of positively charged protons and zero-charged neutrons, with a number of 'shells' of orbiting, negatively charged electrons.

● An electron

○ A proton

● A neutron

The Atom of Hydrogen

The Atom of Helium

Thus our solid matter is mostly space in which the particles are moving so fast that, like the whirring blade of a propeller, they appear solid. In fact, if a propeller was flat and rotated fast enough, it would appear to be as solid and flat as a disc of metal. If it oscillated rather than rotated, it would also have all the characteristics of being stationary. You could even bounce a ball off it. It is an interesting fact that super-high speeds of oscillation or vibration have the appearance and properties of being still. If you add to that the forces between and within atoms, then you can understand further why our physical universe appears so real.

In fact, modern physics does not stop with the classical theory of atomic structure. When we probe deeper we find that the macroscopic parallels and observations of our sensory perceptions do not hold up in describing the structure and properties of sub-atomic matter. Our basic building-blocks of atoms become less solid the further we investigate. They are considered as wave packets, as electromagnetic force fields, as energy relationships. They have 'spin' – they rotate about the axis of their movement. They have an 'oscillation', like an ultra-high-speed pendulum. Whilst spinning and oscillating, they move around relative to each other, in three dimensions. They also have an 'electrical charge' and a 'magnetic moment' and therefore an 'electromagnetic field'. They have qualities known to physicists as 'strangeness', 'colour' and 'charm'.

Human devices and our bodies, too, are really nothing but energy transformers or manipulators – whether they are motors, heaters, refrigerators, buildings, chemicals or whatever, we are just re-arranging the energy patterns, doing little more than playing cosmic mud-pies.

Energy and matter are quantifiable – by weight, temperature, volts, gauss etc – and all these units are inter-related. Indeed, Einstein gave us the basic formula:

$$E = mc^2$$

Where the amount of energy, 'E', in units known as *ergs*, obtainable from a weight or mass, 'm,' is defined as the 'mass' times the velocity of light, 'c', squared. This means that just seven kilograms of any substance – a small sack of potatoes, for example, transformed without energy loss into electrical power, would provide enough electrical energy for the 172 billion ($10^9 \times 172$) kilowatt hours (approximately) consumed by the people and industry of the British mainland in one year. Just for fun, you might also like to know that this is equivalent to 120 million, million horse power or about 200,000 horses per person, per year!

There are many ways of transforming energy into electrical energy. Gravity is harnessed as falling water in hydroelectric power stations. Coal or other fuel can also be burnt, and the heat transformed into electricity. In nuclear power stations, we use our knowledge of the structure of the atom to release energy as heat, which is then transformed into electricity. Actually, nuclear energy sources rely on the *instability* of certain elements which decay or change into other elements, releasing in the process a tiny amount of their weight as *radiation*. Some of this radiation is then transformed into electricity.

Radiation

Radiation consists of an energy flow of atomic or sub-atomic particles (e.g. electrons) and/or electromagnetic energy waves such as heat, light, radio and TV signals, infra-red, X-rays, gamma rays etc. It might be of interest for you to see a schematic representation of the electro-magnetic spectrum, as follows:

10^{29}	10^{26}	10^{18}	10^{16}	1.75×10^{14}	10^{14}	10^{12}	10^{10}–10^4	50–0
Cosmic Rays	Gamma Rays	X-Rays	Ultra Violet	Visible Light	Infra Red	Micro-waves Radar	Radio & TV	ELF

The proportions of this diagram being way out and the numbers being the rate of oscillation or vibration in cycles per second.

You will notice immediately that the section we humans perceive through our eyes is tiny. In fact, if this spectrum were considered as a 1000 mile journey (John O'Groats to Land's End by road), then visible light would occupy just one billionth of one inch.

Actually, there is no real upper end to the speed of vibration, it is just that our instrumentation becomes unable to record it. Other species can perceive parts of this spectrum that we cannot. Many insects perceive ultra-violet light, owls can perceive infra-red (so that they can see their warm prey in the dark) and so on. And there is also the interesting phenomenon of blind people learning to perceive colour through their fingers.

This is actually quite readily understandable, because radiation does not just pass 'through' or 'reflect' from other materials, but the action of passing through or reflecting is the result of *interaction* between the materials and the radiation or energies involved. If you have never really considered it before, try looking at your hand, or any object, and understand that it consists of vibrating molecules, atoms and sub-atomic particles that are really nothing more than energy fields or vibrations in which their electromagnetic aspects or properties are both inherent and vital. The matter that makes up your hand has much in common, in its intrinsic nature, with the light that comes from the sun, for example.

Therefore, any energy of a similar nature, and actually that means all energy, will affect your hand or any other matter and will interact with it.

So colour or light or electromagnetic vibration or radiation will automatically affect the energy patterns that we call our fingers. And if our conscious mind is linked to these changes and can interpret them, then it becomes a sense organ. And this seems to be how some blind people can 'feel' colour.

So, very generally speaking, this is how radiation automatically affects us. Not all radiation, however, is harmful. Some is positively beneficial – a sunny day can considerably enhance our feeling of well-being, for example, while the continued absence of daylight soon makes us feel ill. But then the ultra-violet light which gives us a tan is also a cause of skin cancer. So our sensitivities are very finely balanced.

Much of the electromagnetic spectrum is, however, harmful or disharmonizing to life's processes and in any nuclear accident, such as the 1986 Chernobyl disaster, unstable or *radioactive* atoms are released into the atmosphere. These unstable atoms *decay* into other atoms, which themselves may or may not be stable, and in the process they emit both sub-atomic particles and electromagnetic energy waves of a nature which is disharmonizing to biological equilibrium or health.

Nuclear Radiation and Fall-Out

Nuclear radiation may be classified as follows:

1. **Alpha Particles** are relatively heavy, positively charged particles consisting of two protons and two neutrons – the same constitution as an atom of helium gas without its two negative orbiting electrons. In fact, it was Rutherford in 1903 who identified alpha particles as helium nuclei by allowing them to penetrate the thin walls of a glass tube, subsequently demonstrating that the resulting air inside contained minute quantities of helium. Alpha particles can penetrate living tissue, up to a depth of about one millimetre, moving at velocities up to one tenth that of light, but they are slowed down quite readily, being 'heavy' and charged, by their interaction with the molecules and atoms they meet. They are blocked by .02mm of aluminium and are thus readily screened. The main danger from alpha particles is through swallowing or inhalation of radioactive dust which can then find its way to various parts of the body, after absorption through the lungs, intestines or skin.

2. **Beta Particles** were also discovered by Rutherford, in 1899, and were shown in 1900 by Marie & Pierre Curie and Becquerel to be negatively charged electrons moving at speeds around one half the velocity of light. In fact, beta particles possess a range of energies and are associated with neutrino (electrons with no charge) and gamma ray emission. They can also consist of positive electrons or *positrons*. Beta particles are a hundred times more penetrative than alpha particles and require a 2mm thickness of aluminium to stop the most energetic of them. They penetrate flesh up to a depth of a few millimetres and can cause skin problems, though the main danger is to more sensitive organs from swallowing or inhaling beta-emitting particles.

3. **Gamma Rays**, as we have discussed, are electromagnetic energy waves at a higher frequency than light and X-rays. They are highly energetic and penetrative, passing through the body and represent one of the most severe problems arising from radioactive materials and debris. A nuclear explosion also emits an intense pulse of gamma radiation.

4. **X-Rays** are also emitted by certain radioactive materials. They are also damaging.

5. **Neutrons** and other radiation may also be emitted either by radioactive materials or by a specifically designed nuclear or similar device. Radioactive dust and fall-out are not a major source of neutrons, but an atomic explosion emits them in large numbers. Having no charge, they are particularly penetrative and dangerous being able to penetrate within the electron orbits and collide with the nucleus of other atoms. This can cause the struck atom to disintegrate releasing more neutrons, creating a host of radioactive isotopes of various kinds. When there is a critical quantity of neutron emitting radioactive material in one place, these disintegrations form an accelerating and unstoppable chain reaction, resulting in a nuclear explosion. This is the basis of the atomic bomb.

Radioactive Isotopes

Each chemical element such as hydrogen, oxygen, carbon, calcium, iron, lead, uranium or plutonium is defined as such by the number of electrons, protons and neutrons of which it consists. The lightest element, hydrogen (H), for example, consists of just one electron and one proton. This is an unstable atom which expresses its instability by a ready tendency to combine with other atoms – firstly with itself – (hydrogen atoms go about in pairs, as H_2) and then, frequently, with oxygen. In the process, heat is produced as well as light energy and the combined molecule of hydrogen and oxygen is H_2O or water, normally released as vapour. Hydrogen is the major constituent of natural gas that we burn in our homes as heating fuel.

Other atoms consist of varying numbers of electrons,

protons and neutrons which give to each element its characteristic properties. An element is distinguished by the number of protons in its nucleus, thus providing each element with its *atomic number*. Other forms of the element may also exist with additional neutrons. These *isotopes*, as they are called, are frequently *unstable*, decaying to more stable forms with the simultaneous release of energy in the form of radiation. This is known as *radioactivity*. Radioactive isotopes may also decay into a different element, which may itself be unstable and continue to decay, radioactively.

The number after an element or isotope refers to its atomic weight, which varies depending upon the number of protons and neutrons present in its nucleus. Different isotopes, therefore, will be identified by different numbers. Thus carbon 12 is the usual form of carbon, but there are also carbon 10, 11, 13, 14, 15 and 16 isotopes. Carbon 14 is the commonest radioactive form with which we are familiar.

Radioactive Half-Life

The decay of radioactive isotopes is non-linear and is directly related to the quantity of radioactive atoms present in a substance. Thus, the time taken for half of these atoms to decay is known as its *half-life*. This is a fixed period of time and after this has elapsed, the same period is required for one half of the remaining atoms to disintegrate, and so on. Half-lives can vary from fractions of a second to ten of thousands of years or even longer. Naturally, in any environmental radiation pollution, whether from a bomb or a nuclear power plant accident, the half-life of the isotopes released is of paramount importance. Those isotopes with the shortest half-life will provide the initial highest intensities of radiation, since they decay the fastest. But in the long-term, it is the isotopes with the longer half-lives that cause the greater problems.

Note, however, the significance of the half-life. Essentially it means that the return of radioactive material to a non-radioactive state is continually slowing down. If a substance has a half-life of 30 years (e.g. caesium 137), the concentration will have dropped to one half of its original quantity in 30 years, but to only one quarter of that (half of a half) in 60 years and to just one eighth of the original volume in 90 years. So if, for example, the amount of a substance released was eight times more than the background level, then it would take nearly a hundred years for the level to get back to *twice* the previous background level, (the previous background, *plus* the pollution), assuming that the background level is constant. Caesium 137 is, therefore, one of the more worrying constituents of the Chernobyl cocktail.

Strontium 90, one of the radioactive constituents of nuclear fall-out from atmospheric atomic weapons testing has a half-life of 29.12 years, while carbon 14 has a half-life of 5,730 years. Most people have heard of carbon dating of fossils and rocks, and know that it has a connection with the radioactive percentage of carbon found in all organic life forms. Since this percentage is generally fixed, we can determine the age of a fossil or rock by measuring how much carbon 14 remains. Knowing how long carbon 14 takes to decay, therefore, gives us a reasonably accurate assessment of the age of a specimen, assuming of course, that our assumptions regarding the continuity of natural law and the basic similarity of biological organisms over aeons are correct.

So radioactive pollution is a serious, long-term threat to the well-being of our planet and its life forms, to be avoided at all costs. Under natural law, we have no right to endanger the life or even health of our fellow creatures, let alone our fellow humans, other than is genuinely necessary for self-defence or survival.

The Chernobyl Cocktail

The radioactive gas cloud – containing probably hundreds of radioactive isotopes – released during the Russian Chernobyl nuclear disaster of late April and early May 1986, took just one week to reach British shores. The National Radiological Protection Board (NRPB) duly monitored its content and released the following list of seven major isotopes. In order of radioactivity they were: iodine 131, tellurium 132, ruthenium 103, caesium 137, ruthenium 106, caesium 134 and barium 140. Of these, only caesium 137 has a significantly long half-life, of 30 years, as we discussed. Iodine 131 has a half-life of a fraction over eight days.

The cloud hung between 3000 and 10,000 feet above sea level, with the North of England and Scotland most severely affected. Levels were monitored continuously at all British nuclear power stations as well as the NRPB's laboratories in Glasgow, Leeds and at Harwell in Oxfordshire. In the north of Scotland, at Caithness, an increase of 3000 becquerels per square metre of grassland was recorded, while at Harwell, the rise was about 700 becquerels. Rain brings the radioactivity down to earth quite rapidly which is why people were advised not to drink the rain water. Next in line for contamination is vegetation, so fresh outdoor produce had to be washed thoroughly. Then, cattle grazing on radioactive grass rapidly showed levels of radiation in their milk. In Southern England the natural background level was increased by about 25% or less, while in the Lake District, in the North West of England, where fall-out was particularly high, levels of background radioactivity were as much as ten times the normal, with levels of iodine 131 in milk initially between 100 and 200 becquerels, but rising later in certain areas to as much as 1136 becquerels.

This is far above the normal levels of radioactive iodine 131 because its short half-life ensures that it is present naturally in only minute quantities, if at all. In Denmark and the Netherlands, safety levels are set at 500 becquerels, while in Great Britain, the official figure is 2000 becquerels. Drinking milk for one week during these peak periods would have increased a person's yearly dose by 0.7 per cent of their annual exposure, according to provisional figures released by the Department of the Environment. What the figures do not point out is that the iodine would be concentrated in the thyroid gland, significantly increasing irradiation of this organ. To what degree, would depend upon the individual, how much they absorbed and their existing levels of iodine.

Similarly, a person drinking rain water for one week would have received 2.5 per cent of their expected annual dose, while the average additional exposure from the air during one week would have been about .4 per cent of the annual dose. This represents an average increase over the background concentration, of about 50% during this period of just one week, with some British people receiving 1000% more and some an additional dose of only 25%.

The NRPB suggests that overall, the increased levels of radioactivity experienced will be similar to that experienced due to fall-out from atmospheric nuclear weapon's testing during the early 1960's – a statistic that I am not at all sure I feel happy about, whichever way you take it.

I was myself informed by a press officer at the Department of the Environment that no further bulletins were being issued after May 16th, 1986, because "levels had dropped to such a low level that there was no need to continue issuing data". In view of the high levels in the Lake District, at least, of caesium 137, with its 30-year half-life, such a statement makes little sense. Indeed, the full implications of long-term radioactivity have yet to be appreciated.

During the two and a half weeks, up to May 16th, about one thousand milk samples were taken, but somewhat less than fifty samples of vegetables were monitored. In central England, only one sample of spring greens was taken, whilst there were no samples at all from the Midlands, Scotland, the Isle of Man or Northern Ireland.

Of this abysmally low number of recordings, the highest level of radioactivity was found in a sample of parsley taken from a field in the east of England.

Yet it was on the basis of these tests that British vegetables were given a clean bill of health.

In the Lake District, apparently Britain's worst hit area, grassland recordings were made of 44,000 becquerels per square metre for caesium 137 and an additional 24,000 becquerels per square metre for caesium 134, yet only one cabbage and one cauliflower were sampled. Pasture levels such as these are more than five times those at which the NRPB recommends that cattle should be removed from the fields, yet no government department would own the responsibility of making this recommendation to farmers, so cattle continued to graze.

So all in all, it is quite clear that the British emergency

measures for dealing with leaks of radioactivity are totally inefective. A disturbing fact, considering Britain's twenty-one nuclear power stations.

Let me state it very clearly and simply. There will be negative health effects from caesium 137 lasting for at least one hundred years. To what degree, nobody knows. And where the greatest concentrations have come down to earth – nobody knows that either. And how caesium 137 will migrate through food chains is also very much of a mystery.

The full amount of radiation released at Chernobyl may never be known. It is possible that up to a million curies escaped – enough to cause rapid lethal damage to anyone within fifteen miles and to be responsible for cancer in a high percentage of the population in a far wider area over the coming years. It is probable, however, that the Russians were very lucky on a number of accounts. In particular, the temperature of the reactor core would very likely have been in the region of 2500°C. This would mean that the escaping gas would have risen high into the atmosphere before being blown away from the scene of the accident to descend downwind. And fortunately for them the wind was blowing away from the densely populated area of Kiev, to the east. But let us hope, at least, that radioactive levels and associated health problems are properly monitored in all the countries affected, for we have a distinct lack of knowledge of real 'safe' levels of radioactivity and at least some advantage can be gained from this disaster by using these unfortunate exposures for research purposes.

Safety Levels

Radiation at any level, background or otherwise, is always damaging to body tissues. Extrapolating probabilities downwards in a linear fashion from incidences of known exposure to higher levels of radiation, of which there are extremely few – mostly Hiroshima and Nagasaki – it is estimated that about 2% of cancers in Britain, around 2000 cases, can be attributed to existing background levels of radiation, while the individual risk of developing cancer during one's lifetime is about one in three. So the question becomes – how damaging is just a little? How little is just a little? And how safe is safe?

Well, the honest answer is that nobody really knows because our process of estimating makes so many assumptions of which we cannot be sure. We do know, however, that 'safe' levels are continually being revised downwards. Early workers with microwave radar, observers of the first nuclear explosion on Christmas Island, the inhabitants of Canonsberg, Pennsylvania, site of a 1940's uranium-enrichment factory, the cast and set of the film crew including John Wayne, Susan Hayward and Clark Gable that were downwind of a Nevada desert nuclear test – all these groups and others too, who have received a one-off dose of radiation many years previously, all show high incidence of cancer and leukaemia often ten, fifteen or twenty years later. The evidence, actually, is incontrovertible but no government or company is willing to take responsibility for the manslaughter of thousands of innocent people. But the 'safe' levels of exposure have definitely been reduced from those of the 'early' days, when some people actually thought that low doses of radiation, especially X-rays, were probably quite good for you.

Everybody, of course, is different. This is why not everybody exposed to low levels of radiation subsequently dies of cancer. Those who are weak, who do not live a healthy lifestyle or are more susceptible for one reason or another stand a higher risk of cancer in the subsequent years. We shall discuss these aspects more fully in chapter four. But generally, the levels of cancer are extremely high in our modern world. There are so many carcinogenic substances that we consume without knowing it. Each one may be within 'safe' limits, but the combined total of exposure to carcinogenic pollution is clearly far too high. We have to act fast to clean up our planet and perhaps something positive can come out of an *international* incident like Chernobyl if we are all drawn closer together as one human family, to co-operate in this aim.

The absence of openness by both our own as well as the Russian authorities is also a matter for concern. But one can appreciate their problem. The 'authorities' just do not have a ready solution to the economic, social and health aspects of contaminated agricultural and pasture land, not just in the short but in the long term, because they themselves cannot know either all the facts, or how to interpret them. Naturally, a disaster area or areas has to be declared with no produce grown or supplied until levels of radioactivity reach a certain point. But with the presence of caesium 137 and its 30 year half-life, how long will this take and how wide should be the area and how closely will it be monitored? And what of the dairy products from contaminated land, as well as fresh vegetables and fruit in the soil at that time and reaching maturity later in the year? And if these kinds of measure are stringently introduced, then why at the same time can companies still be permitted to sell tobacco or lead-polluting petrol or fruit and vegetables contaminated with insecticides and herbicides, or other food containing so-called safe levels of preservatives, many of which represent a definite threat to our health? The ramification of factors often leaves us with little choice but greater or lesser compromise.

In Britain, new lower safety levels were introduced in 1985. These were based on a report by the International Commission on Radiological Protection which recommended a safe-exposure level for the general public of between 1 and 5 millisieverts (msv). 5msv was considered the absolute maximum permissible, while a recommendation of 1msv was considered the better value to adopt. Britain took 5msv as its highest permissible dose, while West Germany accepted .35msv and the USA settled on .25msv.

These figures, however, are based almost entirely upon estimates of radiation received by Hiroshima victims and subsequent deaths that can be directly related to the nuclear explosion. *Deaths*, mind you, not even non-lethal cancers, let alone the effects on general health and vitality. Now, however, recent and more accurate computer-modelled assessments of the levels of radiation received by Hiroshima victims indicate that the previous assessment was at least twice as high as the levels that the victims actually received, which means that all previous 'safety' levels should therefore be halved.

Secondly, the degree of sensitivity amongst people varies by a tremendous amount. Even radiologists in hospitals are aware that about 10% of their patients are ultra-sensitive to radiotherapy and exhibit far more pronounced side-effects than other patients. Similarly, research on exposure of tissues in culture to radiation damage shows considerable differences in damage between identical tissues, but taken from different people.

Safety levels for radioactivity take little or no account of these highly sensitive people – about 1 in 10 of us – whilst safety levels of other toxic materials most definitely do. City levels of carbon monoxide from exhaust fumes, for example, are set at concentrations that are still safe for the high risk cases of men over forty-five with special heart problems. A further factor of times three should therefore be applied to the safety levels, making them currently six times higher than they should be.

Finally, they take no account of non-lethal cancers caused by the bomb, for which a further factor of two should be applied.

All this means that the safety levels derived from the Hiroshima data require revision downwards by a factor of at least 12 ($2 \times 3 \times 2$).

If we add to this the general deterioration in health and vitality that does not manifest as cancer, but may simply weaken the individual, we may need to reduce these so-called safe levels by a further factor of ten, a hundred, or even a thousand.

Even cosmic and background radiation will cause damage to health, so how can any 'acceptable level of risk' be really arrived at?

Britain generally has a very poor record on safety levels. Our water pollutants exceed many EEC safety guidelines, our foods contain nearly twice as many harmful food colourants as other EEC countries, including the toxic azo coal-tar dyes. We even use preservatives that are banned in other EEC countries and have no E number allotted to them, so that they are listed by name if at all. Certain food additives used in Britain have no legislation controlling them and therefore they need not even be listed on the food label. And Sellafield is the dirtiest power station in the west, with levels of alpha-emitting radioactive isotopes 1000 times higher than those from American reactors. Sellafield emits radioactive gas from its cooling towers and dumps quantities of radioactive waste into the sea. And, as one might expect, there is an incidence of child leukaemia in the area, nine times normal.

One American radiation expert commented that when he read the report of the Sellafield levels of radioactive emission, he thought it must be a typing error. Sellafield, situated off the Cumbrian coast in the north-west of England, made a serious error of judgement when they thought they could simply dump the waste into the Irish sea and let it get diluted to safe levels out in the Atlantic. In fact, alarmingly high concentrations of radioactivity have been found in the silt washed up in the nearby coastal areas, as well as in fish and molluscs on the sea coast. Sheep grazing on the salt marshes of the nearby Raven-glass estuary have also been found to be seriously contam-inated with radioactive caesium 137.

It seems, too, to be a most remarkable coincidence that the highest levels of radioactivity from the Chernobyl accident were recorded in the Lake District, near Sellafield. The Institute of Terrestrial Ecology has just recently found high levels of caesium 137 on the mountain sides, though whether from Sellafield or Chernobyl is not totally clear.

One is often surprised by the approach which measures safety levels by the numbers who die. Is not quality of life and well-being more important than longevity? And if a certain number die, it is certain that an even larger number will suffer some level of health deterioration. But how to measure well-being? Many folk do not even know what it *means* to feel really good inside themself or to experience excellent physical health. So perhaps they hardly notice environmental factors which pull them down. The human body is remarkably adaptable and can go on living in quite intolerable circumstances, but that adaptation to poor or reduced levels of health resulting in a lowering of general well-being without serious illness is practically impossible to monitor. But if man was at any time a strong, glowing, healthy and vibrant being then there are certainly not many of them left in our modern society. Just go out in the street and take an honest look at people's faces.

So we have to take personal responsibility for our own health and well-being. Concerning environmental pollu-tion and modern living circumstances that we cannot overcome, if we can take practical personal measures then I think we should take them. My book, *A Harmony of Science and Nature, Ways Of Staying Healthy In A Modern World* suggests many helpful methods of keeping in shape, physically, emotionally and mentally, under modern living conditions.

Natural Background Levels

Throughout the history of our planet, man has been exposed to natural sources of radiation of both terrestrial and cosmic origin. These are thought to be one of the prime factors in the spontaneous mutations giving rise to modification of characteristics amongst the species, allowing them to adapt to changing environmental conditions.

1. **Cosmic Rays and Particles** emanate to a great degree from the sun, but radiation from the stars also reaches us, as well as general space debris from indeterminate sources. They consist largely of sub-atomic particles that can also interact with our atmosphere, producing secondary radiations – mainly electrons, mesons (a category of sub-atomic particles) and gamma rays.

Cosmic radiation varies from geological location to location, as well as from time to time. It considerably increases with altitude, since the atmosphere acts as a sponge to cosmic particles. The dosage at sea level is about 0.02 – 0.04 rads per year while at 5000 feet it is twice this level and at 10,000 feet it is double that at 5000. In space itself, the levels are three to eight hundred times the minimum background levels on earth, reaching 7 to 15 rads per year. At a height of several thousand kilometres from the earth lie the doughnut-shaped Van Allen belts, consisting largely of protons and taking their existence from the effects of cosmic radiation. These would give you a radiation dosage of up to 1500 rads per year, if you lived up there. Quite enough to kill you pretty rapidly and representing a problem to all astronauts.

The sun itself is our single most potent source of cosmic radiation. The stream of cosmic particles that emanate from the sun is known as the solar wind and is responsible for most of the natural electrical phenomena of our planet. This includes the Van Allen belts, the ionosphere (a layer of ionized atmosphere about 50 kilometres up), the Aurora Borealis, the multitudinous electric storms taking place on our planet at all times, the electrostatic field between the ionosphere and the earth which contains physiological and psychological stabilizing oscillations known as Schumann Waves, and other more obscure electrical phenomena.

Sun spots and solar flares are intense electrical and nuclear events in the sun and dramatically increase our dosage of cosmic radiation. Sunspots have a cyclic period of about 11.1 years and there is considerable evidence linking times of extreme social unrest, wars, etc., with sunspot activity. The psychological, mental-emotional influences of radiation are an area little explored by western countries and are very difficult to quantify. However, as we will see in chapter three, electromagnetic radiations of comparatively low intensity can and do effect our inner well-being. And psychological energies, of course, can reflect outwardly as pathology in the tissues and organs of the body, as all those who have observed psychosomatic events can tell us. Actually, our whole existence is a psychosomatic event – what is within is automatically reflected outwardly in our body and actions, but not everybody is sufficiently observant to see what is really so obvious.

2. **Radioactive materials occur naturally in the soils and rocks** of our planet, in some areas more so than others. Background levels from such sources vary from 0.025 rads per year in 'ordinary' regions to as much as 2.8 rads per year in certain areas of the world. French granite has levels up to 0.35 rads per year, Swedish houses built using alum shale materials can deliver up to 0.22 rads per year, whilst monazite[1] alluvial deposits in Brazil can reach 1 rad per year and in Kerala, India reach the currently recorded maximum of 2.8 rads per year.

We should also point out that there are certain areas of the world that have a high incidence of cancer without there being any readily observable cause, as well as those where there is an obvious cause such as a nearby nuclear power station. There are other more subtle energies, often called earth energies, that can cause good or bad atmos-

[1] A rare earth metal mineral composition containing cerium, lanthanum, yttrium and thorium phosphates

pheres or vibrations and subsequent good or bad health.

3. **Drinking water**, too, can contain radioactivity varying from region to region by a factor of 10,000 and **foods** may concentrate particular minerals and elements into their tissues. Seaweed and dairy products, for example, will concentrate iodine, radioactive or otherwise, while nuts and cereals have a higher concentration of radium than meat and animal flesh. It is estimated that we receive about .06 rads per year from natural radioactivity ingested via our food and drink.

4. **The air we breathe** also contains naturally occuring carbon 14 as carbon dioxide, as well as radon 222 gas, adding a further dose of about .08 rads per year.

All in all, therefore, we receive about .2 rads per year in the United Kingdom, with the granite areas of Aberdeen, Devon and Cornwall, being amongst those localities with the highest levels of natural background radiation. The *rad*, is a measure of the actual amount or dose of radiation absorbed by living tissues, while the *rem* is a measure of its biological ionizing effect. In man, these are normally considered more or less equatable. The *sievert* is a new unit equal to 100 rems and the becquerel is a measure of the actual number of radioactive disintegrations per second. These units are more fully defined in the next chapter.

Artificial Levels of Radiation

Man's activities on our planet, largely from nuclear explosions and testings, nuclear power plant accidents, continuous low-level emission into the air from nuclear and coal-burning power stations, inland waterways and the sea, nuclear batteries, high-voltage power supplies, smoke detectors, TV sets and computer terminals, etc., have all resulted in an increase in radiation levels that if present trends continue will result in the entire human population being exposed to at least twice the original background level by the end of this century.

If one also considers the continuous low-level bombardment from TV and radio broadcasting, electrical cables, motors and other devices, then one estimate of our current degree of radiation is as much as 200 millions times that which our ancestors absorbed from natural sources just one or two hundred years ago. Our lack of real knowledge leaves us with no clear idea exactly what kind of effect all this energy will have on our vitality and health.

Statistics are often given which average out the doses of radiation we receive from medical and other artificial sources, amongst the entire population. So when the United Kingdom Atomic Energy Authority issues figures that state that the nuclear industry contributes no less than 0.002 rems per person, 0.1 per cent of the background levels, it obscures the fact that radiation levels around the Sellafield plant in the Lake District, especially on the coastline, are high enough for general warnings to be given for people to avoid the beaches in the area as much as possible.

After all, if the total radioactive emission from the Russian Chernobyl accident were averaged out over the entire world population, a statistic could be produced that would show no appreciable risks to anyone at all. But the fact is that some of the victims received massive lethal doses of up to 800 rems and even in the north of England, levels reached ten times the normal.

So what is of interest to us, personally, is not average statistics, but how much *we* are getting, *individually* – a question no-one can really answer.

For example, levels of radiation experienced due to atmospheric atomic weapons testing peaked during the mid-1960's reaching a maximum of .008 rems per year, 4% of the background level and sufficient to cause enough anxiety for atmospheric tests to be discontinued. But we may never know how much particular sections of the population received, since the figure of .008 rems is, of course, a global average. We do know, however, that all human beings absorbed detectable amounts of caesium 137 and strontium 90 from levels reaching up to thirty-five times the levels to which these two isotopes had declined by the late 1970's. These magnitudes being recorded both in atmospheric deposition as well as in milk. These two isotopes, by the way, are not normally found in nature, so *any* level is above the 'normal'.

Generally, it is supposed that inhalation, ingestion and skin absorption represent the major means by which we absorb radioactive isotopes, especially – in order of magnitude – from milk, cereals, meat, poultry, fruit, green vegetables and root vegetables – the proportions and exact order varying depending upon the isotope in question. Iodine 131 is highest in milk, for example, whilst carbon 14 is highest in cereals and flesh foods.

In medicine and dentistry, radioactive isotopes and X-rays are also used to a considerable degree. A normal chest X-ray for example, will give you a dose of 0.04 to 1 rad per exposure, whilst a gastrointestinal X-ray delivers a full 1 rad. Limb X-rays give between 0.25 and 1 rad, but don't forget that your red blood cells are produced in the long bones of the body, so your limbs play an integral part in total body physiology. Fluoroscopy delivers 10–20 rads per minute and an X-ray movie about 25 rads per examination.

All these levels are not enough to cause immediate and obvious symptoms of ill-health, except in severe radiotherapy or excessive use of X-rays, but as we discuss in the chapter three, the more subtle and long term effects of these energies are of some considerable concern.

There is, however, a little-known source of dangerous radioactivity which can affect us in our modern insulated homes.

Radon Gas

A article by Robert Matthews in the *New Scientist* of December 5th 1985 discusses the pollutants that can accumulate in the atmosphere of our draughtproofed, insulated homes. There are many, and one of them is the radioactive and carcinogenic gas radon 222. Radon is invisible and comes from the decay of naturally occurring uranium 238, a common element found in traces in most soil, bricks and building materials. Radon 222 has a half-life of about 3.8 days, decaying to two isotopes of polonium, also radioactive, which when inhaled irradiate the lungs with alpha particles leading eventually to lung cancer. In certain parts of the country, Devon and the Pennines in particular, there is a considerably higher level of uranium, resulting in dangerously high levels of radon building up in draught-proof houses.

In fact, the NRPB have been conducting a survey of radon concentration in homes with some disturbing preliminary findings. They have found homes that have levels 10 times that of the NRPB's recommended safe limit, exposing the inhabitants to as much risk of lung cancer due to radon gas, as to all the other cancers combined. At least 1000 homes probably exceed the existing safe limit by smaller degrees and a further 100,000 homes exceed the level at which action is advised by the Royal Commission on Environmental Pollution.

Danger Units – A Way of Combining the Safe Limits of Exposure to Toxins, Mutagens and Carcinogens, also Relating them to our Lifestyle

In the light of the foregoing, it would seem a logical step to formulate a *combined* safe level of exposure to the various undesirables present in our food, drink, air and environment as a step upon the way to eradicating them entirely. Supposing a new unit were specified; let us call it – to emphasize the point – the *danger* unit. Each substance would then be ascribed so many units of *danger* per unit weight, or volume or rad or whatever. If this were then a part of food labelling laws and if levels in our environment were regularly published, we could easily work out to how many units of *danger* we were exposed on a daily, weekly, monthly or yearly basis. With limits of *danger* suggested at which vitality and health were threatened, we would soon begin to see why cancer and heart disease have already reached epidemic proportions, and why AIDS is threatening to be such a world-wide killer. The major threat to the people of our planet lies in biological degeneration caused by poor diet, incorrect living habits and pollution of the environment. These are the reasons for the increase in degenerative diseases that are besetting us. Man has never been perfect in his social structure, at least not in any recorded history, and all civilizations have ultimately crumbled, their strengths often later proving to be their weakness and their undoing.

Lifestyle, too, would need to have units of *danger* ascribed to it, with healthy practices – eating wholesome foods and practising meditation, for example – receiving negative values, while stressful lifestyles, eating junk foods, drinking alcohol, smoking tobacco and drug-taking would receive positive *danger* units. A clever piece of computer programming could handle it quite readily and it would represent a kind of rough assessment of how well we are living and how safe or unsafe are the levels of environmental pollution.

A Confusion of Facts

If you feel confused over the various figures, safety levels and estimates given, this is not surprising! It is a direct reflection of three factors:

1. Nobody fully understands how radioactivity harms us, what levels – if any – are safe, and why its effect varies from person to person.

2. Statistics can be greatly misleading, even in the hands of those who want to communicate the full truth of the matter. For example, if you refer back to the figures given for the Chernobyl accident, you will see how radioactive levels in milk, at least several hundred per cent higher than usual, can be averaged out to a dosage of 0.7% of yearly exposure in a week when related to all forms of background radiation. Expressed as 0.1% per day this figure looks even better, whilst the increase in concentration of radioactivity dosage of all kinds, not just the milk, during the period of this one week, but averaged out over the year, comes to about 5%. This may or may not be significant, biologically, but it represents a difference in dosage magnitude of a factor between 25 and 1000 per cent, during the critical week, depending on where you were. So you can readily see how a large figure can be expressed as a small one, and vice versa.

3. Government and the nuclear industry are so committed

to the use of nuclear power that I do not believe we are given the full facts in an open and simple manner. It is significant that the NRPB was freely handing out information to the press at the beginning of the Chernobyl incident, but that they were later silenced by the government, with all enquiries routed through the Department of the Environment (who refused to give interviews to the press or TV). The effect of the Chernobyl incident has been to create widespread public concern over the use of nuclear power, something the government would prefer to quell. An accident similar to that of Chernobyl at the Sizewell Nuclear Power Station in Suffolk, for example, would cause problems in East Anglia, London and the home counties, (not to mention France, Belgium and Holland just across the Channel), very much the same as that faced by the far less densely populated areas of the Ukraine.

At the end of 1985, 382 nuclear power stations were in operation, worldwide. Of these, Britain has the highest density, with 21. Europe, in all, has 210 nuclear power stations – 143 in Western Europe – 13 of which are clustered in northern France, Belgium and Holland, just a few miles across the English channel. Western Europe has a further 44 nuclear power stations under construction.

With the implications of nuclear accidents being brought home to us and especially with all central European countries except France imposing a ban on the sale of milk and green vegetables in the wake of the Chernobyl accident, opinion polls have revealed that the vast majority of European people feel that nuclear power should be phased out – 69 per cent in West Germany, 70 per cent in Holland and 79 per cent in Italy. In France, Europe's largest country, with the highest number of nuclear power stations – 39 operational and a further 20 under construction – the French government failed at first to publish figures on the increased levels of radiation. Surely a direct reflection of their dependence upon and commitment to nuclear power and of a fear that their people would, on quite rational and logically acceptable grounds, reject the nuclear approach.

So however safe nuclear power stations may be, I

wonder if it is reasonable – with so many nuclear power stations worldwide and with an increasing level of their use in Third World countries – to assume that that the necessary degree of safety is maintainable over the next fifty or one hundred years? Accidents *will* happen. Three Mile Island and Chernobyl will not be the last. Accidents are in the nature of the world, a built-in part of the great cosmic dance

CHAPTER 2

Biological Effects of Radiation

Having described how radioactive emissions will interact with the energy of atoms and molecules, being all of the same essential nature, we now need to see how this is worked out in biological organisms and what are the problems created. The key to a simple understanding of this lies in an appreciation that our bodies, like everything else, are vibrating and moving energy structures. Harmony and easy flow amongst these energy patterns leads to health, well-being and inner happiness; whilst disharmony, blockages and breaks in this flow constitute disease or ill-health, along with feelings of tiredness, depression and unhappiness.

The true aim of any physician, therefore, should be to create harmony amongst the energy patterns in our body, mind and emotional complex. This will lead to health and well-being. It follows naturally that any symptomatic approach to healing is doomed to failure, since the underlying disharmony in the energy patterns is simply suppressed and will surface somewhere else within that individual. A symptom is a 'cri-de-coeur', a red warning flag or a hand raised. To gag the screamer, remove the red flag or chop off the raised hand will not solve the problem, it will only compound and suppress it. In fact, the deeper we are as personalities and in our understanding, the less superficially do we approach any aspect of life – health or otherwise.

There are really two interconnected ways of understanding the energy interchange processes that take place in our human organism. Firstly, there is the biochemical and electrobiological approach and then, moving inwards into more subtle realms of energy, we can view the harmonies and disharmonies created in our subtle energy blueprint, which is discussed in chapter three. Then we need to examine various ways of building up our strength and throwing out toxins etc., at both of these levels. That will make chapter four of this little book. But first, let us define some of the units of radiation you have encountered.

Units of Radiation Measurement

1. The *roentgen* is a measure of exposure to radiation, based upon the capacity to cause ionization. One *roentgen* of radiation is defined as that quantity of radiation that produces a specified number of charged ions in a one cubic inch of air under standard conditions. An *ion* is a molecule or atom that carries an electrical charge due to the gain or loss of a (negatively charged) electron. Radiation is classifiable as *ionizing* radiation if it is energetic enough to damage molecules and atoms by stripping off their electrons. These free electrons can then cause a number of biological problems. Most radioactive emissions are ionizing radiations, as are X-rays and higher frequency electromagnetic radiations.

2. The *rad* is a measure of the actual amount of radiation of all types, absorbed by living tissues themselves. It is a unit of energy, equal to 100 ergs delivered to one gram of tissue. An *erg* is a basic unit of energy in which all other energy units (watts, mass, etc.), can be expressed. Human tissues absorb approximately one rad when one roentgen irradiates one cubic inch of it, so when considering humans, one rad is pretty much the same as a roentgen.

3. The *rem* (**r**oentgen **e**quivalent **m**an, abbrieviation: *r*) allows one to define (to some extent) the degree of biological effect, because the same dose in rads, but from different sources of radiation, will have different biological effects. Clearly 100 rads of sunlight will have a different effect from 100 rads of gamma rays. The *rem*, therefore, is defined as that dose of radiation that produces the biological effect in man of one rad of X-rays. This is clearly a pretty loose kind of definition since it assumes that we know what the biological effects of different forms of radiation actually are.

In the modern system of units, the rem is replaced by the *sievert* (sv), where one sievert equals 100 rem. A *millisievert* is one thousandth of a *sievert*.

4. The *becquerel* (bq) is a direct measurement of the number of radioactive disintegrations per second. e.g. 1000 becquerels per square metre means 1000 disintegrations per second per square metre.

5. The *curie* is a standard of radioactive emission based upon 1 gram of radium in which there are 3.7×10^{10} nuclear disintegrations per second. So if a quantity of radioactive isotope has one curie of radioactivity, it means that it has the same degree of radioactivity as one gram of radium. Radium was chosen as the standard because of its long half-life, plus the ability to get it in pure form.

Metabolism and The Effects of Radiation

Our bodies, as we have described, are a vast complex of energy interchanges. Looked at on the biochemical level, we see an almost infinite variety of neutron-proton-electron, atomic, molecular and electromagnetic patterns. But what makes our body tick is its ability to transform the energy from the foods we eat into chemical energies that constitute our body's processes and movements. This process is known as *metabolism*, or more specifically *aerobic metabolism*, because oxygen forms an essential part of the process. In particular, it involves the transfer of electrons from one molecule to another, a process known to science as an *oxidation–reduction* reaction. The molecule which loses the electron is said to be *oxidized*, whilst the molecule which gains it is *reduced*. This process is finely tuned and orchestrated through the catalytic action of enzymes, the controlling influence of hormones and a host of similar energy interchanges, so that just the right amount of energy is produced at the right time and in the right place. The final acceptor of the electron is oxygen, which is how the process received its name. Our nutrient input or body fuel is, therefore, in quite a real sense, burnt for the production of energy, burning being an energetic oxidation of materials.

Now, as an integral part of this process, certain highly energetic and reactive molecules are created. These are known as *free radicals*, or unbalanced bits of molecules.

An electron carries a negative charge, whilst a proton carries an equal and opposite positive charge. Molecules and atoms within our bodies are generally balanced electronically either within themselves or in conjunction with a molecule or atom carrying an opposite charge, due to the gain or loss of an electron. These molecules or atoms with a charge are known as *ions*. However, if an unbalanced molecule, a *free radical* is let loose without proper biochemical control, then we have problems. Electrons are most harmonious when orbiting in pairs, each with an opposite spin direction, but *free radicals* usually have an unpaired electron. This means that they are ready to combine with anything that is remotely suitable and in the process, they can break up other molecular structures, including cell walls and structural proteins, generally disrupting the normal cellular and hence bodily processes.

The body, of course, has its own police force and scavengers for dealing with these bad guys under normal conditions, but if the individual is at low par for whatever reason, then more serious damage can be done to the tissues.

The effect of radiation follows a very similar pattern. The alpha and beta particles carry an electrical charge which disturbs the bodily molecular and atomic electrons in their orbits, causing *ionization* and a resultant series of disharmonious and destructive biochemical reactions. Cell membranes can be ruptured, electrical potentials disturbed, structural proteins such as collagen damaged, DNA and other parts of the cellular intelligence and information system can be dimembered and depending upon the intensity of the irradiation, minor or major chaos will result. Cells carry the unique intelligence and ability to reproduce themselves. This information is contained within the cellular nucleus, in the DNA molecules that constitute the chromosomes and if this informational blueprint is damaged, then further generations of cells will likewise be imperfect.

This means of course that those tissues in the body which reproduce rapidly will be more open to immediate symptoms of irradiation. This includes blood cells (red and white from the bone marrow, white only from the spleen) and explains the symptoms of anaemia and leukaemia that rapidly develop in irradiated people. Other rapidly proliferating cells are found in the intestinal linings, as well as in the basal layers of the skin.

When these epithelial cells suffer damage or there is inhibition of the continuous reproduction required of them, then their protective role is severely weakened leading to inflammation and ulceration, fluid loss, diarrhoea, nausea and general invasion by toxic substances, bacteria and viruses. Hence, intestinal and skin cancer, as well as hair loss, are also amongst the earlier symptoms of longterm degeneration to manifest. Skin cancer, especially amongst the white skinned races, is also caused by ultraviolet radiation, the same radiation which causes a sun tan, so habitual sunbathers and users of ultraviolet sunbeds, be warned.

Children and developing embryo's are particularly at immediate risk because their continuing and active growth will immediately proliferate any damage done to the biochemical blueprint. Mutations are also more likely in the reproductive germ cells and naturally any genetic misformation at this stage of development will result in abnormalities of a greater or lesser degree in the child and later the adult. Actually, mutations due to low level intensity may not even show up for several generations, by which time the original cause will be untraceable.

In adults, the effects can be immediate or may not show up for ten, fifteen or twenty years. This exposure to low levels of radiation is known to cause cancers many years into the future and a number of these instances are discussed in the book, *Subtle Energy*. Skin and other cancers have even been known to occur up to forty years after causative exposure. But quite apart from the biochemical damage, there is another angle that is characteristically overlooked by more conventional approaches to the problem. This can be called our subtle energy system and is discussed briefly in the next chapter and in much greater detail, once again, in the book, *Subtle Energy*.

In laboratory animals, exposures of as little as a few roentgen can destroy the spermatazoa of mice, wake up snoozing rats when played on their olfactory organs and increase the incidence of siezures in mice genetically prone to them. It is also reported that irradiation of one organ can effect the functioning of other organs. From a wholistic as well as conventional medical viewpoint, this is readily understandable, so it comes as no surprise to find, for example, that irradiation of the liver and spleen upsets nucleic acid metabolism at other sites in the body. The body is, after all, one complete interacting and interfunctioning network of energy interchanges.

Genetic Problems and Radiation

Our biochemical blueprint is stored as a coding in the sequential arrangement of substances known as amino acids within the complex double-helix molecules of DNA (Deoxyribose Nucleic Acid) that go to make up our chromosomes. These molecules contain the genetic code that defines the way we look externally, as well as the myriad internal biochemical processes that go on within the cells of which our physical body is comprised.

Radiation can break up these molecules, which may then recombine in a correct or incorrect order. Pieces can even get deleted in the process. Since this genetic code is responsible for the maintenance of healthy cell division, any disruptions can cause problems if the abnormalities are reproduced. Spontaneous mutations are a part of nature and the body has its own ways of dealing with these mistakes, but naturally, if the mutations are of too great a number or if the body's defences are down, then that individual is at severe risk of developing cancer either now, or at a later date when the mutated cell population reaches a critical threshold.

Mutations in the reproductive germ cells represent a risk by which exposure of the parent is built into ensuing generations. These may be immediately apparent, or may be dormant or recessive, perhaps only coming into activity when two such children have children of their own, though studies of the children of Hiroshima and Nagasaki survivors are claimed to show no such higher incidence of radiation-induced genetic abnormalities.

Target Organs

Certain organs and tissues of the body are more at risk than others because of their tendency to store and concentrate particular elements that have radioactive varieties or isotopes. For long-lived isotopes that are not eliminated from the body, this can clearly cause cancers and health damage at some, perhaps distant, time in the future.

Iodine is perhaps the commonest element quoted in this connection. It is an essential constituent of thyroxin, a hormone produced by the thyroid gland in the neck. The thyroid tissues store iodine for use when required and, naturally, a concentration of radioactive iodine 131 is undesirable and can lead to thyroid cancer. This is why iodine was handed out to people exposed to radioactive iodine during the Chernobyl disaster, so as to take up the available storage space in the thyroid before the radioactive variety came along. Iodine reaches the thyroid within six hours from ingestion and remains there for up to 120 days.

Personally, I would have preferred to see doses of iodine-rich herbs and vegetables or natural tablet preparations made from these, being used, rather than neat iodine, which is a highly reactive element, though practicalities probably made such a move impossible, even if considered. Natural, synergistically bound remedies will create more general body harmony amongst its multitudinous energy patterns than neat, inorganic substances.

Caesium 134 and **137**, like iodine, can be absorbed through the lung membranes or from the small intestine. They spread rapidly throughout the tissues, forming particular concentrations in the muscles. Around 10% of ingested caesium is excreted within two days, but the remainder is eliminated only very slowly, with half still remaining after four months. Sheep grazing on Cumbrian salt marshes contaminated by radioactive pollutants from Sellafield were found by the Institute of Terrestrial Ecology to have high concentrations of caesium 137 in their kidneys, while lambs which had clearly been grazing for considerably shorter periods had far greater quantities.

Strontium 90 is absorbed in similar fashion and makes its home on the surface of the bones, initially replacing calcium in the bone cells, from where it migrates throughout the entire body skeleton becoming a potential cause of leukaemia, anaemia and blood-related cancers, through irradiation of the bone marrow.

Carbon 14 is absorbed from our diet or inhaled as carbon dioxide. Radioactive carbon 14 is the main radioactive isotope released from British Magnox reactors, whence it rapidly finds its way into food chains – carbon, hydrogen and oxygen being the chemical basis of organic life on our planet. Ubiquitous in bodily distribution, carbon 14 from dietary sources can get more or less anywhere in our body and can remain with us for long periods of time. Carbon dioxide gas, on the other hand, is dissolved in the blood via the pulmonary capilliaries (blood vessels in the lungs that absorb oxygen and release carbon dioxide), but is then exhaled within minutes along with the normal bodily elimination of carbon dioxide.

Other organs that store concentrations of elements with radioactive isotopes are the kidneys which accumulate **uranium**, and bone tissue which concentrates **radium 226, plutonium 239** and many other radioactive materials, where they can cause problems to the bone itself as well as the blood cell manufacturing that takes place within bone marrow. **Hydrogen 3 (tritium)** is found in water and is hence ubiquitous in the body. The ovaries and the testes are also particularly sensitive to all water soluble isotopes, while tiny radioactive particles in suspension can end up in the spleen, bone marrow or liver.

Finally, there is **radon 222**, a radioactive gas that can cause breakdown of the pulmonary lining, as well as lung cancer. Radon has already been discussed in the previous chapter.

Short Term Biological Symptoms and Lethal Doses

The degree of radiation that can kill rapidly is said to begin at around 100 rems (equivalent to rads in humans) though below this level any radiation will still have ionizing, heating and disharmonizing effects which – depending upon the health of the individual – will be combatted to varying degrees. The Russians have made considerable research into the biological and behavioural effects of low intensity microwaves as well as radio and TV broadcast radiation. This is discussed briefly in the next chapter. Natural background levels of hard radiation probably total around .05 to .25 rads per year, depending upon the locality.

At intensities of between 100 and 200 rads, immediate symptoms, appearing within a few hours, are vomiting, headaches, dizziness, loss of appetite, general debilitation and weakness – more or less what you would expect from a severe disharmonizing of the whole body system. Within a few weeks, problems are seen in the rapidly reproducing tissues – the bone marrow which makes the red blood cells and the spleen and lymph glands where the white blood cells are manufactured. Death is not usually imminent, though as the years go by the exposure will take its toll in decreased vitality and a high risk of cancer, depending upon the individual. The reproductive germ cells will also have been effected and any children subsequently conceived will carry a higher than average risk of genetic deformities.

Above 200 rads, death in the short term, within two weeks to three months, is an increasing likelihood. The onset of vomiting and loss of vitality are rapid. Anaemia, low white blood cell count, loss of hair and skin irritation are expected symptoms and with exposures above 600 rads, death will occur in 90% – 100% of victims. Over 1000 rads, symptoms appear within minutes with increasing severity, and death is the result in all cases. There are severe gastro-intestinal problems, and the nervous system along with the body's electrical potential system and brain function being increasingly damaged. Victims exposed to doses greater than 5000 rads can be expected to die within a few days.

These kind of intensities are fortunately only experienced during intense radiation – nuclear explosions and their subsequent fall-out or continuous exposure to radioactive materials. There is absolutely no known way of putting the body's scrambled atomic and molecular structure back together again after this kind of intense radiation.

CHAPTER 3

Radiation, Subtle Energy and Electromagnetism

Subtle Energy

I deliberated for some time before I put in this chapter, because there may be a significant number of people who might find the concept of subtle energies difficult to follow or understand and come to suspect the verity of the remainder of this book, by inference. But then, true things should not be hidden just because they may raise a few eyebrows. So read it through if you will, but if the cap doesn't fit – then don't wear it! Most of it is taken from the books, *Subtle Energy* and *A Harmony Of Science And Nature*.

Modern man is by now well acquainted with the fact that the physical universe as perceived by our five senses is very different in appearance from that which is described by science. This scientific description has changed and is continually changing.

Other species inhabiting this planet have senses which we lack, for their perception of physical energies: some birds have a sense which perceives the magnetic grid of the earth and they use it for migration. Other creatures perceive wavelengths and frequencies of sound and electromagnetic energy (eg. light) that we cannot. Dogs, horses and other animals seem to have a 'sixth sense' – they are aware of the subtle energy vibrations of humans and their fellow creatures as well as other parts of the electromagnetic spectrum.

Furthermore, even amongst humans, we differ in both our perceptive abilities and in our interpretation of the perceived data. Some people have a far higher frequency range in their hearing than others. Some are colour-blind, an artist sees colours more vividly, musicians may have 'perfect pitch', some have altogether lost one or more of their senses and an increasing number are tuned to the subtle vibrations of objects and people. Our mood and state of health and well-being also affect our perceptions. In other words, what we perceive is not a fixed reality, but a subjective experience based upon our own physical, emotional and mental make-up.

The proposition then, that there are energy fields and patterns of which we are – through our five regular senses – unaware, should at least be acceptable to us as a working hypothesis. We still switch on our TV and are happy to use a remote control without ever perceiving anything 'coming into' our home or passing from our remote-control device to the TV set! Indeed, we can still use electricity without understanding its nature and governing laws.

Our physical universe is a mixture of both perceivable and imperceivable 'gross' matter and more subtle energy fields. Subtle energy fields are the blueprint of physical matter. Our physical body is actually two bodies. The gross physical body, perceivable by the five normal senses, and the subtle – sometimes called etheric – body of which the physical is a precipitation or reflection downwards. The state of the subtle body determines the health of the physical body. In high energy physics terminology, the subtle energy is the 'ghost'–energy from which physical matter is derived. Some physicists these days talk of 'ghost' electrons, for example. No scientist has ever demonstrated the existence of a 'ghost' electron, but theoretically, its reality would seem to be essential to scientific thinking and rationality. In Nature, you cannot get 'something' for 'nothing'; for an electron or any sub-atomic particle to exist, there must be something to substantiate it, or give it its energy. That is its 'ghost' or subtle counterpart.

According to a theory put forward by some physicists, the link point, the window or zero-point between subtle energy and gross physical matter, is in the spin and movement of sub-atomic particles.

All sub-atomic particles are in constant motion, they spin and move in three dimensions. One can say that the movement of energy in three dimensions is what makes physical matter 'solid' or 'real'. This physical universe is

47

motion, action, cause and effect – *karma*, as the Indian yogis and mystic philosophers call it.

Now this spin and movement of sub-atomic energy patterns can vary, without any external visible signs of its change in state. In other words, the inner state of kinetic being within sub-atomic matter can vary without the five normal senses being able to perceive any difference. In high energy physics terms, this duality of our life – light and darkness, heat and cold, happiness and sorrow, life and death – is reflected in the harmony or disharmony of vibration in sub-atomic and allied energy fields which in turn is a reflection of the polarities in subtle matter.

In our bodies, the state of our subtle energy determines our degree of health and emotional/mental well-being. In our environment, the harmony or disharmony within subtle energy and the sub-atomic energy patterns, gives rise to the experience of good or bad atmospheres or vibrations. Our physical bodies then, are comprised of the gross physical of which we are easily aware and the subtle or etheric, the blueprint of the physical, which controls our state of health in the gross physical. Healing can therefore take place in two directions – by controlling the gross physical which will change the polarities in the subtle and/or by changing the polarities in the subtle which will reflect downwards and manifest as the creation of healthy tissues in the gross physical. In practice, those involved in the healing professions, consciously or un-consciously, use a mixture of both. And the reverse of the process, the disharmonizing of energy fields can likewise take place from within-out, as well as from without-in.

Subtle Energy Terminology

Throughout the literature on subtle energy topics, we encounter a wide variety of names used in its description. Just as the physical universe displays an endless show of shifting and changing energy patterns, part of which we discern through our senses, so too in the subtle energy fields do we find a spectrum of energies. Different ther-apies seem to deal with different aspects or areas of these energies. Being beyond our five physical senses, they are more difficult to chart and the names used to describe them can become confusing. I use 'subtle energy' to describe all subtle physical and super-physical energies up to the level of mental or thought vibrations. Other terms, some specific, some general, are: etheric, Ch'i, prana, bio-energy, auric force field and many more.

Bodily Polarities

All of nature, all our human science, all our activities and those of the cosmos are all underlaid by the principle of duality or polarity. Our universe, our bodies, our emotions, our minds and thoughts are all comprised of gross and subtle energy fields in vibrating and pulsating motion. The cause of this motion is difference – polarity or duality. Even physics tells us that the apparently solid and stationary objects around us are no more than vibrating energy fields of sub-atomic forces – of positive and negative electrical charges, of north and south pole magnetic fields. Motion exists because of this inequality. Energy, in an eternal cosmic dance, seeks a state of balance. High moves to low, positive runs to negative, clockwise is balanced by anti-clockwise and as it moves, it experiences a force pulling it back to where it was and so it vibrates, orbits or oscillates, like a swing or like the planets.

In Hindu terminology these three states of matter are known as the *Gunas. Rajas Guna* is the attribute of activity, of creation, of coming into being. It is springtime, life, restlessness, extrovert, centrifugal, expanding, hot, positive. *Tamas Guna* is the condition of inaction, of destruction, of moving out of being. It is autumn and winter, death, introvert, centripetal, cohering, cold, negative. *Satvas Guna* is the state of balance or harmony between the two. It is peace, equanimity, apparent changelessness; but it can also be disturbed at any time. Therefore it is temporal and bounded by the transitory nature of existence and is also a state of tension.

The interplay of these three intrinsic forces is manifest in all aspects of existence – inner and outer, in nature as well as our inner lives. The spiritual goal of life lies in transcending the spheres of mind and matter where these three principles hold sway, of moving into the domain of oneness, where peace is intrinsic and not acquired, is absolute – not relative.

But the essence of healing our human ills lies simply in creating harmony amongst the energy patterns of our human constitution. Once this principle is firmly established and understood, then it becomes only a matter of subtle or gross mechanics, of 'how?'.

As in all energy systems, our human constitution has inherent and specific natural polarities, at both electrical, magnetic and subtle levels. Very briefly, there are three basic subtle energy patterns or circuits in the body, with their in-built, driving polarities. There are:

1. **The Mental Circuit.** This controls the brain, the head, the main sense organs, the throat and speech. It is particularly strong in intellectual and highly rational people and is linked to these mental faculties; the brain and sense organs being its outward physical manifestation.

2. **The Emotional Circuit.** This controls the heart, lungs, liver, kidneys, spleen and solar plexus. The energy being derived from that in which feeling and emotion manifest, hence the expressions 'Have a heart', and so on. Emotional upset can result in heart problems or manifest in the solar plexus ('butterflies'). There are numerous connections known to doctors of all callings between our emotional life and the manifestation of physical problems or disease.

3. **The Physical Circuit.** This controls the pelvic area, including the sex organs, the legs and hands. It is usually the most powerful energy present in physically oriented people.

What Effects Subtle Energy Harmony and Polarity?

Because all energies are interconnected both within ourselves and in our environment, all the processes of life, including just being alive, will affect subtle polarities. These include:

1. Food and Water.
2. Air, especially its levels of pollution and ionization.
3. Mental and emotional attitudes and energy, our personality.
4. Electromagnetic radiation.
5. Bio-entrainment.
6. The earth's magnetism and more subtle earth-energy fields.

The full effect of these factors cannot easily be discussed in this short chapter and a fuller summary is contained in the book, *Subtle Energy*. Of all these, let us consider in greater detail the effects of modern, electromagnetic radiation, along with its inevitable counterpart of bio-entrainment. In this chapter, I am talking mainly about the effects of the non-ionizing radiations which are around us all the time from radio and TV broadcasting, electric fields around cabling, electrical devices and high tension power lines. Radioactive emanations will have similar effects on the subtle body as well as their more obvious effects on cellular metabolism, which is actually only a reflection of the energy structure at a deeper vibration.

Vibrational and Electromagnetic Pollution

Polarities and harmony in the body's subtle energy fields are affected by exposure to electromagnetic radiation of all frequencies and wavelengths.

This can be readily understood. Sub-atomic matter is currently seen by modern physics as energy patterns and forces, vibrating at speeds approaching that of light. Indeed, this kinetic energy is an inherent aspect of its being. The forces that hold it all together are also an essential part of its existence. These forces are electromagnetic, gravitational and allied fields. Powerful cosmic rays and particle emissions are already known to alter atomic structure even in a macroscopic sense – molecules and atoms are changed permanently – as we have described, this is part of the effects of radioactive emissions.

It is highly likely, therefore, that all electromagnetic energy, including light, affects the movement of the energy patterns at sub-atomic levels. Since the sub-atomic energy and electromagnetic energy are of the same nature, they will attract and repel; they will interact; they will not be indifferent to each other.

Sub-atomic and electromagnetic energy are the first physical manifestations of subtle energy. The vibrational states of subtle energy will affect the sub-atomic energy patterns and vice versa. Hence it comes as no surprise to find that electromagnetic energy affects the polarities in our subtle body and causes changes in our level of health and well-being. This need not all be negative, however it does seem that it is only the wavelengths of natural sunlight to which our own bodies and systems are attuned. Outside of these wavelengths, we start having problems. These polarity reversals and energy disturbances can remain at the subtle level or manifest, sooner or later, as biochemical and physiological problems, including cancer.

The case of the film set who were irradiated by radioactive fall-out when the wind changed direction during a U.S. Nevada Desert atomic explosion test has become quite well-known. Now, fifteen to twenty years later, many of the cast and film crew are dying or have died of cancer. Similarly, with the ground zero engineers who were ordered into the area before it was contamination free. In Hiroshima, even forty years on, victims are still contracting cancer and dying of the effects of the weapon used so long ago. This phenomenon of delay is generally accepted, scientifically, though not fully understood.

Recent research in the England around the village of Fishpond in Dorset has also identified a higher than average incidence of suicide and psychological disturbances amongst people living within the very high electromagnetic induction field surrounding high voltage electricity pylons. In the U.S., a higher than average incidence of leukaemia has been related to the proximity of high voltage pylons. Higher rates of leukaemia have also been observed amongst high voltage power workers, as well as amongst short wave amateur radio enthusiasts.

There are many cases that can be quoted. The point is that this kind of electromagnetic pollution may not show up in serious illness for as long as fifteen to twenty years, even forty years, after the event. Furthermore, it is very difficult to quantify the effect of continual bombardment by low intensity electromagnetic radiation such as TV and radio broadcasting and ordinary mains circuit emissions in domestic and commercial properties.

There have recently been a number of reports indicating a statistically significant proportion of miscarriages and embryonic deformities amongst expectant mothers working on VDU's – computers and word processors etc. In fact, a young woman has recently won her appeal against unfair dismissal because she refused to work at a VDU when pregnant. After hearing all the evidence, the adjudicators ruled that she had ample supporting evidence for her decision, which was fully justifiable. So not only might the electromagnetic fields and radiations from VDU's be causing molecular and perhaps even chromosomal damage, but the delicate fabric of electrical potentials in the body and in the brain are most certainly modified by the electric field surrounding TV's and VDU's.

There are many parallels, too, in other areas of environmental pollution. DDT, for example, was heralded as a boon to pest control. However, it was later found to be harmful to human health and the recommended quantities to be used by farmers were drastically reduced. Later on, as it became evident that DDT is stored in the body over long periods, is both poisonous and carcinogenic, and is also non-biodegradable so that it remains in the soil year after year, it became a 'non-recommended' (not illegal) chemical. I remember that as a child, we used to waft the DDT around in the same free and easy manner that we now use modern cleaning powders. There was always a cannister of DDT under the sink. Now you cannot buy it in the shops anymore, though farmers can still obtain it and similar pesticides.

Indeed, radium itself was once used as a 'cure' for arthritis and other diseases, though when it was discovered that it was also responsible for anaemia, bone cancer and other problems, the practice was discontinued. This was in 1930 and the Radium Hospital had been founded in Paris in 1906, twenty-four years earlier.

Similarly, what is discounted today as unharmful electromagnetic radiation may, in the light of further evidence, prove to have highly injurious effects on our long-term health and well-being. It would be interesting to have accurate statistics on the relationship between the high incidence of cancer and heart disease and the build up in usage over the last three decades of electrical appliances, computer, VDU and electronic equipment and especially TV and radio signal broadcasting and receiving.

But it is not just the emissions of electrical appliances and TV/radio broadcasting, however, that cause problems. All metal objects and electrical conductors, including our bodies themselves, act as aerials for electromagnetic radiation, just like the TV aerial on the roof of one's home. Electrical currents are induced in tooth-fillings, buckles, jewellery and zippers on our body as well as in all the metalwork in our homes and offices – electrical wiring, water pipes and, most importantly, in the coiled springs inside mattresses. Since we spend one third of our life asleep, this factor is of some importance.

Bio-Entrainment

The bio-energy, subtle force field or aura of the body is also affected by sympathetic resonance with similar force fields. This partly explains, for example, why husband and wife who have lived together for many years can take on very similar features in both physical appearance, as well as in mental and emotional attitudes. They are living within each other's aura and their energy vibrations become attuned to each other.

We are also affected by the presence of other people on a day to day basis. Note also how moods can take over an entire crowd or room full of people. We talk, too, of atmospheres – good or bad – that build up amongst groups of people. We also find that certain places, homes or individual rooms have 'good' or 'bad' vibrations and affect us accordingly.

When this effect is long term, it creates a habit in our body known as *bio-entrainment*, a form of subtle energy resonance, and while we may be happy to be uplifted by good vibrations, we would prefer to avoid the drag of the negative.

Entrainment of brain and body functions can also occur from electromagnetic radiation. The heart, brain and muscles all emit signals from less than one cycle per second to over a hundred thousand cycles per second. These signals form the basis of electrocardiograms and electro-encephalograms. Amidst all this electrical activity, four predominant brain wave patterns can be identified:

Delta	0.5 to 3Hz	Deep sleep, higher states of consciousness
Theta	4 to 7Hz	Reverie, dream states
Alpha	8 to 13Hz	Passive, blank, relaxed, meditation
Beta	14 to 30Hz	Thinking, active mind and/or body

ELF (extremely low frequency) electromagnetic emissions at these frequencies are thus likely to be psycho-active. That is, they can affect your mood. It is said that the USSR and the USA have both developed and use such weapons. They call it 'world mood manipulation' and 'psychotronic warfare'.

A 1984 TV documentary revealed that the Soviet Union has built the three largest broadcasting stations ever de-signed. From these stations are broadcast a pulsed electro-magnetic signal that is receivable as a click on a shortwave radio. This is the most powerful electromagnetic signal ever broadcast. The given code name is 'Woodpecker' and both the U.S.A. and Europe – but not the U.S.S.R. – are targets for this emission. The U.S.A. have responded by building a similar transmitter, the signals from which are bounced off the ionosphere, but the Soviet Union now have many years research behind them on psycho-active, electromagnetic frequencies.

Very little research has really been made in the West, but in Russia and Eastern Europe, hundreds of experiments have shown that electromagnetic fields and waves such as we experience every day due to TV and radio broadcasting may cause a host of health problems, including blood disorders, hypertension, heart attacks, headaches, sexual dysfunction, drowsiness and nervous exhaustion. The book, *Electromagnetic Fields and Life* by Dr A.S. Presman from the Department of Biophysics, Moscow University, describes in detail many such experiments, with full details of biochemical tests performed. It was first published in

Russian in 1968 and translated into English in 1970.

One of the most interesting of Dr Presman's discoveries is that greater biochemical effects are often caused by *lower* intensities of irradiation, whilst the effect of higher doses can sometimes cause less biochemical changes – at least in the aspects he was monitoring. What this means is that *danger levels are not always equatable with quantity*. This is something that should cause a stir amongst those setting safety standards. Perhaps it can be understood through the analogy of a key, which has to be of exactly the right dimensions to cause the desired effect. Too large or too small a key is useless. If a key does not fit, simply bringing a bigger one will not solve the problem.

In support of this theory comes the fact that *pulsed* electromagnetic fields and waves are often more danger-ous than a continuous and uniform radiation. It is the *pattern*, rather than the *power* that is of greater importance. There is even evidence to suggest that certain diseases have certain patterns, electromagnetically, that can be induced in the body by beaming at it the appropriately modulated electromagnetic energy. If individuals, too, have a unique electromagnetic fingerprint, then one can appreciate why different people are effected to varying degress by the same level and frequency of radiation dosage, because some are disharmonized more than others in their electro-magnetic and more subtle energy fields.

But whatever the mechanisms, as a result of their experimentation, the Soviet Union have strict rules over the amount and duration of emission from radio trans-mitters and radars that a person can safely absorb. The West has only an informal, non-legal guideline set in 1966 by the U.S. American Standards Institute. The Soviet criterion is one thousand times more stringent than this for workers and ten thousand times more for civilians. Clear-ly, the Russians believe that even small doses of electro-magnetic radiation, over time, can do considerable harm.

A rather unfortunate example of the effect of non-ionizing radiation occurred during the 1960's and 1970's,[1]. In 1962, the American CIA discovered that the Russians were irradiating the office of the U.S. Ambassador in

[1] *The Menace of Electric Smog*, Lowell Ponte, *Reader's Digest*, U.S.A. edition, January 1980.

Moscow with microwaves, from two buildings across the street. The level was .002 of the level that the American guideline called unsafe.

Setting up an experiment upon monkeys, duplicating this irradiation, the Americans found within a matter of weeks that there were adverse effects upon the animals' immune and nervous systems. Embassy personnel were not at this stage advised of the problems, but were requested to give blood, 'testing for a disease in Moscow's water'. It was found that over half of them had a high white blood cell (lymphocyte) count – symptomatic of severe infection as well as of leukaemia.

It was not, however, until 1976 that the U.S. government took remedial action. Declaring the site 'unhealthful', they erected metal window screens to shield out the microwaves. But this was fourteen years after the discovery and now it is said that these embassy personnel exhibit a higher rate of cancer than the average and that two U.S. ambassadors who served during this time have subsequently died of cancer.

It is of concern, therefore, that in the U.K., we can boast not only microwave cookers and microwave radar at airports and military establishments, but also a recently installed microwave cloud mapping system scanning the country and used in weather forecasting.

Similarly, it seems likely that part of the computer and video 'junkie' syndrome, affecting many people, has its roots in an addiction to the electromagnetic radiations and voltage potentials around the VDU. Finally, let us add that subtle energy polarities are reversed by crossing the earth's magnetic lines of force, this being one of the causes of jet-lag and premature ageing in air-line pilots and air-hostesses. It is one of the reasons why an east-west or west-east flight has a worse effect than a north-south journey.

What I am trying to get at is that there is plenty of evidence that low intensity, non-ionizing radiation does have a detrimental effect on living organisms through disturbance to the polarities and harmony in the body's minute electrical and electromagnetic fields as well as in more subtle energy fields. It may not cause death in a statistically significant number of people, but it does change the way you feel and your level of well-being.

Remember that all the safety levels for radiation are set based on causing *minimum deaths*. Not one of them takes any account of the levels of vitality and well-being.

CHAPTER 4

Natural Protection From Radiation

There is no complete antidote to the health problems caused by radioactivity. In this instance, prevention is certainly better than cure, since high levels of exposure will kill. Lower levels of ionizing radiation will cause the damage that has been described, BUT the health of your body and the vitality of your biochemistry and physiology will determine to a large degree how well your body can cope and how readily it can throw off the effects of molecular damage. This was born out by studies of the Hiroshima and Nagasaki survivors, as we shall see.

Therefore, the approach we should take should be to strengthen our bodies as much as we can and to use whatever specifics we know about that will strengthen the body's natural resistance to ionization, oxidative action and toxic compounds, as well as both physical and subtle energy disharmonies.

Avoiding Radiation

Depending upon where you live and what information can be gleaned on the extent of the problem, you should avoid drinking rain water after any nuclear fall-out has been detected. Tap water should in any event be purified, preferably distilled, prior to drinking. Distillation is nature's natural way of water purification by evaporation of the water from impurities, followed by subsequent condensation and precipitation in the form of rain. In time of nuclear accident or otherwise, rain becomes contaminated when it washes the radioactive materials out of the atmosphere. These days, tap water and often rain water, too, is heavily polluted and no longer fit for healthy human consumption. Just think of the deposits left by rain on buildings and trees, as well as the effects of acid rain on trees, waterways and lakes. Domestic water filters only partially solve the problem, leaving behind a number of serious carcinogenic pollutants, including nitrates.

Milk also comes in for continuous testing after nuclear pollution because cattle feed directly on grass which has had radioactive materials washed into it by rain. Therefore, it is also a good idea to avoid milk and dairy produce from contaminated areas for a while.

Fresh vegetables should be thoroughly washed, but what to do about vegetables grown on contaminated soil in later weeks, months and years depends upon the concentration and half-life of the contaminants. Ideally, their content should be monitored and if it is significantly above the background level, I would be inclined to avoid it. The problem is knowing the level of contamination. There is no easy answer to this. One way of looking at it is that we are already consuming so much pollution in our food that as long as it is just a little, it won't add much to the already adverse conditions in which we are living – not a satisfactory state of affairs. A recent study of fruit and vegetables, for example, found that one third contained DDT or its similars. DDT is toxic, carcinogenic and generally detrimental to health along with many other pesticides, herbicides and preservatives that find their way into our foods.

My wife, Farida, and I have, over the years, devised a number of ways for staying healthy in our modern polluted world and much of this is documented in our book, *A Harmony of Science and Nature.*

So basically, in times of specific radiation hazard, keep out of the rain, drink pure water and be thoughtful of the food you are eating.

Anti-Oxidants

You will remember that one of the ionizing effects of radiation is to release free radicals and free electrons that then run riot within the cells. Anything, therefore, which absorbs these molecules and electrons is of great help. Fortunately, considerable research has been and is being made on anti-oxidants, but it must be remembered that simply taking one or two anti-oxidants will not readily solve the problem. Biochemical processes are a complex system of molecular interchanges and any nutritional supplement, to be really in harmony with nature, must bear this in mind. That is, it must ideally be a part of an organically integrated and balanced complex in as natural and unadulterated form as possible.

Commonly mentioned anti-oxidants include vitamins C and E, selenium and beta-carotene, the latter having a proven ability to reduce the risk of lung cancer in smokers. Further anti-oxidants include many of the Vitamin B complex, zinc, glutathione and the sulphur-containing amino acids – cysteine, taurine and methionine, for example.

Selenium is an essential trace element required only in ultra-minute quantities, but working along with vitamin E in the maintenance of balanced metabolic activity. It is also prized by seekers of youth because it enhances tissue elasticity through inhibition of the oxidation of poly-unsaturated fatty acids that can result in stiffening of structural tissue proteins. Selenium is also involved in the process of elimination of heavy metal atoms from the body, a useful factor to bear in mind in regard to radiation.

Part of the problem with radiation-induced damage lies in its ability to knock electrons out of water molecules, leaving free hydroxyl (OH^-) ions. These then become highly oxidative peroxides capable of damaging the sulphur-based groups found not only in certain amino acids, but also in enzymes such as catalase that are involved in the anti-oxidant process. But as long as there are enough sulphur-based groups present as amino acids, to combine with peroxides and free radicals then the enzymes may be spared. The de-structured amino acids are then converted to other harmless substances and are either eliminated or re-used in other ways within the body's biochemical system.

Germanium, a trace element found particularly in ginseng and garlic, has a similar anti-toxin and anti-radical activity in the body. Dr Kazuhiko Asai has had remarkable success with the use of an organically bound germanium compound synthesized in his Japanese laboratory; this work is documented in his book, *Miracle Cure – Organic Germanium*.

Germanium is an interesting atom with unusual properties due to an unstable outer shell of four electrons. It is this structure, for example, that gives it its semi-conductor properties used in transistor and diode technology, most probably utilized by the body, too, as a part of its delicate bioelectrical system.

Dr Asai believes that lack of oxygen, the final acceptor in the oxidation-reduction pathways, is responsible for many degenerative disorders through the build-up of acidic, H^+ radicals in the body and associated toxins. Because of its unique structure, germanium acts as an alternative to oxygen, attaching to the H^+ radicals. The germanium is then eliminated from the body, with the toxic radical in tow. Indeed, germanium is completely removed from the body within twenty to thirty hours.

Interestingly enough, germanium is also found in remarkably high concentrations in *Trametes cinnabarina*, a fungus reputed to be efficacious in the treatment of cancer and mentioned by Nobel prize winner, Alexander Solzhenitsyn in his book, *Cancer Ward*.

Finally, there are also certain artifical anti-oxidants – preservatives, actually – and some folk do take these. Personally, I feel happier acknowledging my own essential ignorance of nature's processes and therefore taking substances already in naturally balanced form.

For this reason I have always preferred taking freshly prepared fruit and vegetable juices to tablets prepared from even natural sources. This way one takes in a host of nutrients that are definitely fortifying though nobody knows quite how. The whole is definitely greater that the sum of the parts and especially just a few parts, perhaps synthetically prepared.

Some people occasionally ask why a person should take juices, when they can consume the fresh fruit or vegetable directly. The answer is, of course, that with juice you are consuming the highly concentrated nutrients from far more vegetables than you could ever begin to consume at a meal. You can consume the nutritional essence of several pounds of produce, *in addition* to your regular diet. This way you get a concentrated balance of vitamins, amino acids, minerals, trace elements and much more besides.

But make sure you get a proper juicer. Centrifugal juicers may only deliver a third of the nutrient made available by a true, non-centrifugal, masticating juicer. Even the pulp from such a juicer can be made to yield considerably more nutrient when the resulting pulp is put through a special, hydraulic press. A centrifugal juicer may in fact only yield one sixth of the available concentrated nutrients. Juices should be taken before or between meals and you can readily take up to two pints a day.

Juices and foods which are *high* in the above anti-oxidants include the following, with (★) identifying an especially good source:

Vitamin C	Citrus fruits (★), apples, broccoli, brussels sprouts, cauliflower, cabbage, apricot, celery, cucumber, garlic, kiwi fruit (★), onion, papaya, parsley (★), pineapple, radish, rhubarb, spinach, tomato (★), turnip leaf(★), watercress (★), watermelon (★).
Vitamin B Complex	Cabbage, carrot, celery, coconut, dandelion, garlic, grapefruit, lemons, parsley, pineapple, radish, watercress, wheatgerm, brewer's yeast (★), yoghurt, sprouts, beans, peas and nuts.
Vitamin E	Spinach, turnip leaf, watercress, wheatgerm (★), milk, cottage cheese, olive oil, soy bean oil, green leafy vegetables, raw fruits.
Selenium	Wholegrain cereals, garlic, mushrooms, broccoli, onions, tomatoes, nuts, asparagus. Toxic in anything other than minute doses. The amount of selenium in vegetables depends upon the quantity in the soil upon which they are grown.

Beta-Carotene	Carrots (★). A precursor to vitamin A.
Zinc	Milk, wholewheat flour, wheatgerm, pumpkin seed, brewer's yeast. Toxic except in minute quantities.
Sulphur	Kale, cabbage, cauliflower, brussels sprouts, garlic, leeks, onions, cucumber, spinach, horseradish (★), watercress, carrot, celery, romaine lettuce, parsley, coconut.
Germanium	Aloe vera, chlorella, comfrey, garlic (★), ginseng (★), *Trametes cinnabarina* (★★).

Juices have the added advantage, too, of not only providing concentrated and balanced nutrition, but also being high in prana or subtle energy which further fuels your level of vitality, helping to throw off the effects of any damage due to radiation or other cause. Dr Norman Walker, the great proponent of fresh-pressed vegetable juices, was reputed to be 108 years old and still going strong when last I heard of him.

However, if you find the thought of making juices too much trouble (actually, it is quite easy) then there are a number of vitamin and mineral supplements available in health food shops, but try and get the most natural available and those without fillers. As to quantities, it is best to follow the maximum recommended doses, with the exception, perhaps, of vitamin C. Vitamin C is water soluble and once the cells are saturated with it, the remainder is excreted from the system via the kidneys and urine. There is said to be an advantage in taking mega-doses of vitamin C to combat illness and you could try taking up to 10 grams per day, but it is best to find a pure form since the fillers used are not a natural nutrient and can cause digestive irritations.

The Immune System

The immune system is that part of our biochemistry and physiology that protects us against invaders – microbial or chemical. It is also responsible for removing toxic wastes from cells and in de-activating them or helping in the process of their elimination. The orchestration of this process comes through interlinking and feedback between the thymus gland – a small organ that lies just above your heart – the pituitary gland and the hypothalamus in the brain, the other endocrine glands, amino acids, vitamins, minerals, trace-elements and the general biochemical energy network.

From the thymus gland, until only recently considered an evolutionary vestige with no function, comes the hormone *thymosin*. Thymosin stimulates the maturation of the T-cell lymphocytes, (lymphocytes are also known as leucocytes or white blood cells) manufactured in the bone marrow, which directly combat the effects of micro-organisms, carcinogenic and toxic chemicals, and radiation-induced biochemical disharmonies – free radicals and their ilk. This is why one of the earliest responses to irradiation and electric fields is an increase in the number of lymphocytes. The body is trying to do something about it.

The thymus itself is directly connected to the higher centres of endocrine and nervous control in the brain, so that physical, biochemical and also emotional stress cause an increase in its activity.

T-lymphocytes produce hormone-like molecules known as lymphokines which biochemically attack all invaders, one of these being interferon, a compound being used with some success in combatting cancer cells. T-cells also stimulate another variety of lymph cell, macrophages, which function as biological scavengers, ingesting and swallowing up whatever nasties they can.

B-lymphocytes, produced in the spleen and lymph nodes, locate foreign organisms and make specific anti-bodies – biochemical destruction and deactivation agents – against them. This antibody system is a part of the body's protection against bacteria, viruses and potential allergens, and is the basis of the science of immunology. B-lympho-cytes are a remarkably adaptive and creative munitions factory with the ability, within limits, to create new biochemical weapons as new invaders are encountered. And once created, these weapons stay with you. This is intelligence at the biochemical level and explains why you only get certain diseases once in a lifetime. After that you have the right antibody to fight the virus, bacteria or allergen should it attempt a second landing.

The turnover of lymphocytes is prodigious. There are perhaps a trillion of them in a normal healthy body, about two pounds by weight, sustained, owing to their short life cycle, by the manufacture of about ten million per minute. They are ubiquitous and move about in the blood stream, as well as in the lymph vessels and interstitial fluids, bathing the body cells. They can also pass through the blood capillaries, giving them free passage from tissues to blood and back again.

It is very clear, therefore, that any nutrients that particularly fortify your immune system will be of value in strengthening yourself against the effects of radiation damage. And it is not surprising that we find some old friends amongst them.

T-cells hold within them a high concentration of vitamin C which drops markedly with illness or when your biochemistry is under stress from toxic pollution. (e.g. smoking). Intake of vitamin C, therefore, helps you cope with the effects of radiation and it also explains why the energy imbalances caused by continual crossing of the earth's magnetic field on a long east-west or west-east aeroplane journey, resulting in jet lag, are countered by the use of large doses of this (and other) vitamins. It also explains why vitamin C taken *before* illness is of value, because the immune system is thereby fortified.

Similarly, members of the B group of vitamins, especially B_6, B_{12}, pantothenic acid and folic acid, are of considerable importance. Folic acid deficiency in animals has been shown to decrease the T-cell count by up to 80% and folic acid is often lacking in humans, especially women.

Vitamins A and E, as well as zinc and selenium, are once again involved, so the same approach to nutritional supplements is required as with the anti-oxidant program. And once again I personally prefer the use of large quantities of fresh juice and natural nutrients like ginseng, royal jelly and bee pollen to multi-vitamin pill-popping!

Biochemists are no doubt discovering many wonderful secrets, but there are billions of different compounds in the body, enough to keep an army of biochemists busy for centuries unravelling the tangled skein. Nature's innately balanced foods will contain all of these if chosen judiciously and perform many functions besides, of which we are totally unaware in our present state of knowledgeable ignorance. Even biochemists insist on certain supplements being balanced with co-operators on the biochemical scene. Amino acids, for example, need to be taken with some understanding and require the support of various vitamins etc., for their correct assimilation. Amino acids found in foods and juices are automatically balanced in this way.

I do not say not to take supplements at all, but in general, the natural approach will always create better bodily harmony than the unnatural.

Actually, I am continually amazed that nutrition, the basic body fuel for the maintenance of physical life, is so neglected in most hospitals and in most medical teaching and practice. Isn't it surprising that the material out of which the body is made is largely neglected by the medical profession in their attempts to create health? Hospitals should ideally be a healing environment where all aspects of body and mind are *nourished*. There are a few like this in the U.S.A., and other parts of the world, and their success rate is remarkably high. They are also pleasant places to be in. I don't decry the wonderful advances of some aspects of modern medicine. It just needs to be working in closer consciousness with nature. Health is more than just the absence of disease, it is a positive state of vibrant well-being.

Raw Foods and Wholefoods

There is no doubt that the mineral and nutrient intake among those of us using whole rather than refined foods, with a reasonable proportion of raw salads in our diet, are in far better nutritional shape than those eating a junk food diet. The healthier your diet, the healthier you will be and the more able to withstand the effects of radioactive or any other form of 'attack' against your well-being.

Iodine and Kelp

Kelp is a seaweed, high in iodine and is hence a useful way to top up the thyroid gland whenever there is radioactive iodine about. You can buy it in powdered or tablet form, or if you live near an unpolluted part of the sea, you could gather your own. Being a natural, non-toxic food, there is no upper limit set for its consumption and it is also claimed that some of the lignin fibres in kelp and other seaweeds can actually remove radiation from the body. Fibres in general, in all raw and wholefoods, are not only good for a healthy digestive and eliminative system, but they actively draw heavy metals and toxins from the body, including any of the heavier radioactive isotopes. Research at the McGill University in Canada demonstrated the ability of a substance in kelp and other seaweeds to reduce by 50 to 80 per cent the absorption of radioactive strontium 90 from the intestines.

Other foods high in iodine are, in order of iodine concentration: romaine lettuce, cucumber, spinach, tomato, beetroot, pineapple, carrot and pomegranate.

Heavy Metal Blockers and Purifiers

Although the Chernobyl mixture contained nothing heavier than caesium 137 and barium 140, previous atmospheric atomic tests have placed quantities of other, heavier radioactive isotopes into our atmosphere, as well as strontium 90. Heavy metals, as higher weight elements are known, also including lead from exhaust fumes and outdated plumbing, are generally toxic to the biological processes and tend to accumulate in the body, especially the bones, although lead is also responsible for brain damage, especially in children.

There are two ways of approaching the heavy metal problem:

1. As with iodine and the thyroid gland, one can take foods rich in calcium to keep the bones topped up and provide minimal space for the heavy metals to lodge. It

is important to know that up to 32% of available calcium is denatured when food is heated above 150°F (65°C), so pasturized milk is a limited source. Similarly with tinned and junk foods. High sources of calcium are cereals, grains, cheeses, dulse, greens, Irish moss (seaweed), kelp, sesame seeds and raw milk, though many other nuts and vegetables are also excellent sources. Mineral calcium, as found in hard water and some tablets, is best avoided, since it is not organically or synergistically bound and represents a problem for the body.

2. Secondly, one can use substances that help the body to eliminate toxins or heavy metals which may be radio-active and/or toxic. Algin (a seaweed preparation) is a useful starting point here, though any substance which stimulates the lymphatic and immune system will also be of value. There is also a seaweed bath which is said to be helpful in eliminating heavy metals, and selenium we have already mentioned.

I have always found it a matter of great satisfaction when natural foods or herbs that have been used for centuries in traditional medicine and often discounted by modern drug-oriented medicine (there's not so much profit in fresh vegetables) are 'suddenly' dis-covered to contain substances that do just what the traditional doctors always said they did – using differ-ent terminology perhaps, but essentially the same. As you will see in the section on the macrobiotic diet, an active polysaccharide, sodium alginate, that binds to toxins and heavy metals, aiding in their elimination, has been discovered in algin. Yet the Chinese have been using sea vegetables for their drawing and de-toxifying properties for aeons.

Amongst herbs, my herbalist wife uses a specific formula for heavy metal de-toxification consisting of equal parts of yellow dock root (*Rumex crispus*), bugle-weed (*Lycopus virginicus*) and chaparral (*Larrea divari-cata*), with a quarter part lobelia (*Lobelia inflata*). As a herbal strengthener for the lymphatic and immune systems, she uses equal parts echinacea (*Echinacea an-*

gustifolia), lobelia (*Lobelia inflata*), mullein (*Verbascum thapsus*), poke root (*Phytolacca decandra*), burdock root (*Arctium lappa*), cayenne pepper (*Capsicum minimum*) and chaparral (*Larrea divaricata*).

Both these formulae are discussed in her book, *Herbs of Grace*.

Chinese Herbs of Power: Panax Ginseng, Eleutherococcus, Tang Kwei, Astragulus, Ligusticum

When reading through ancient Chinese and Far Eastern descriptions of their herbs and roots, one cannot help but be heartened and uplifted by the depth of their understanding of the energy fields and interchanges that make up our bodies and our environment. They may not express it in our deeply analytical and western terminology, but from their knowledge of natural laws and principles it is quite clear that concepts such as the unified field theory, presently the focus of much attention in modern physics, would have been crystal clear to them. They may not have applied mathematical formulae to their intrinsic understanding, but they definitely possessed and used a great wisdom two thousand years ago, when our British ancestors were still busy battling it out with the Romans.

Civilizations come and go and each one thinks perhaps, that theirs will last forever. Each culture has its areas of wisdom and knowledge, as well as its negative aspects. Our own modern culture is unique in the extent of its geographical spread and therefore its influence on other essentially different ways of life.

With our ability to travel and exchange information at high speed has come the possibility for a merging of cultures, for us to learn from far older and wiser cultures. Science, technology and true wisdom desperately need to be drawn together and if scientific analysis is the forte of our 'New World', then wisdom and understanding of inner human constitution and our place in the eternal energy interchanges of the cosmos is the strength and support of ancient eastern cultures. So we should not be afraid to learn from them.

This merging of cultures is most apparent in scientific studies of ancient Chinese medicine. Chinese herbalism is understood in terms of Ch'i, the universal subtle energy field underlying all atomic and molecular structure. Their herbs are described and prescribed according to their effects on these energy fields. But the subtle fields and biochemistry are closely linked, energetically, in a vertical energy spectrum of creation from within and so it comes as no surprise to find that the most powerful of the Chinese tonic herbs have a wealth of essential nutrients and substances many of which are known to modern biochemistry and medicine as valuable to the healing process.

One group of Chinese herbs far surpasses all others in its general ability to amplify our Ch'i or to tone us up in a natural way. Because of this quality, most easily verifiable by simply taking them and observing the result, modern science has brought them into the laboratory for analysis and discovered some extremely interesting characteristics. Ron Teeguarden's excellent book, *Chinese Herbs of Power*, is well worth reading if you would like more specific and fuller information on these herbs.

Ginseng Root (*Panax ginseng*) is known in China as the king of herbs. It tones up the entire system with an emphasis on the lungs and spleen, also strengthening the heart, liver, intestines, bladder and gall-bladder. Ginseng builds up an organism's non-specific resistance to ill-health, as well as ionizing radiation. It imparts biochemical and physiological resistance to stress factors, permitting a biological adaptability that has earned it and other tonic herbs like it, the modern scientific name of *adaptogens*.

Ginseng is a superbly balanced combination of essential nutrients and biochemical strengtheners. It contains: ginsenin, vitamins B and B_2, saponin, panaxin, panaquilon, panoxic acid and aromatic oils. Amongst its minerals are found: aluminium, barium, calcium, germanium, iron, magnesium, manganese, potassium, sodium and strontium. It also contains: sugars, starches and a number of steroids.

Ginsenin has similar properties to insulin, while the other substances mentioned regulate and stimulate metabolism, the nervous system and cardiovascular function, also preventing a build up of cholesterol. Resistance to infection is also enhanced and there are improvements in both long and short-term memory. Panaquilon balances and tones the endocrine system, probably via the hypothalamic and pituitary controlling glands, while the aromatic oils appear to work directly on the brain.

The steroids in ginseng, like those in certain western herbs, possess a similarity in structure to oestrogen, progesterone and testosterone (the major sex hormones) as well as the metabolic adreno-cortical hormones, such as cortisone. These factors help modern medicine understand some of ginseng's properties.

The Soviet scientist, Dr Breckman, of the Institute for Biologically Active Substances in Vladivostok has shown in his research over many years that a number of these natural tonic herbs and remedies do most definitely increase an organism's non-specific resistance to ill-health, pollution and radiation. He has shown for example, that even a single dose of **Siberian Ginseng**, *Eleutherococcus*, was enough to extend the life of laboratory rats exposed to lethal levels of X-rays. In one experiment, ginseng-fed rats were able to survive up to twice as long as the control group. *Eleutherococcus* is said to have been included in the special diet fed to Russian astronauts and although only a distant relative of *Ginseng panax*, it obviously possesses similar properties. These herbs are clearly strengtheners of the bodily systems and provide the stamina required to cope with the stresses that are placed upon it. Ginseng therefore enhances both physical as well as mental endurance and is used by athletes. Laboratory animals fed with ginseng display these same characteristics and have been demonstrated to outlive their less fortunate counterparts by as much as fourteen per cent.

The quality of ginseng available varies considerably and care is required in its purchasing. In China, the wild Manchurian Tung Pei ginseng, found in the depths of mountain fastnesses, does itself practise what it preaches by living up to two hundred years. The roots are fat and white, up to twelve inches long, and bear a remarkable resemblance to the human body, a factor not overlooked by the Chinese, to whom shape is an important aspect of energy manifestation – just as modern biochemists are interested in the shape that atoms assume in a molecule.

These old roots are slightly radioactive, a fact that could be taken in a number of ways, and are said to glow in the dark. They are very rare and fetch a price of between £2000 and £7000 an ounce. Eat one of these, says the legend, and you will live a long and healthy life.

Imported Chinese ginseng varies considerably in quality, so try and get the pure root from a supplier who really cares about his source.

Korean ginseng has similar properties to the Chinese. Red 'heaven' grade, according to Ron Teeguarden being preferable to the white roots, owing to the manner of its preservation. Korean ginseng is said to be more immediate in its effects and more outward in its results. In eastern terminology, the Chinese ginseng adds energy or fire to the *yin* (negative, receptive, indrawing) aspect, while balancing the *yang* (outgoing, positive) energy. Korean ginseng tones up both. Therefore, it is not so recommended as the Chinese variety for overly active, outward people who already possess plenty of 'fire' energy.

In general, a good ginseng root has a full, rich flavour, distinguishing it from the more insipid, poorer varieties.

Panax ginseng, however, is often spoken of as a man's herb, and while it provides great benefits to women too, the Chinese herb root, **Tang Kuei** or **Dong Quai**, *Radix Angelicae sinensis*, must be the queen of herbs for its superb tonic properties in women – though also providing great tonic effects for men. In clinical trials, Tang Kuei has shown many of the general balancing properties also exhibited by ginseng, such as lowering the blood pressure, slowing the pulse and relaxing the cardiac muscles, but as a specific to bring harmony to the female organs and endocrinology, it is exceptional. For more details, you should read Ron Teeguarden's book.

Astragali radix (*Astragulus membranaceus*) is yet another of the super-tonic Chinese roots that has received scientific attention. Known to the Chinese as a strengthener of the Wei Ch'i, the protective energy that flows beneath the surface of the skin, *Astragulus* has been used with great effect in stimulating the sluggish and deteriorating immune system of cancer patients. A report in *Cancer*, published by the American Cancer Society, reported that 90% of cancer patients who took *Astragulus* in aqueous solution responded with a restoration of their immune function. Radiation, drug therapy and pollution also upset the immune function and scientists now believe that this wonderful herb can be used non-specifically against all degenerative diseases, especially those affecting the immune system such as AIDS, since – among other properties – it reduces the level of T-lymphocyte suppressor cells, found in high concentrations in AIDS patients.

Finally, **Ligusticum**, *Ligusticum lucidum* or *wallichii*, also from the traditional Chinese materia medica, has been found, like *Astragulus*, to possess a powerful stimulant to the immune system and has many other similar properties.

Incidentally, you may be interested to know that in modern Chinese hospitals both 'western' and traditional Chinese medicine are practised side by side and medical students are required to take courses in both kinds of medicine, whatever their ultimate method of practice might be. This would seem to be an excellent and tolerant response to the needs, desires and inclinations of the individual physicians and patients.

These Chinese herbs of power are clearly able to do something that no modern, synthesized drug can do, for they provide a glorious combination of highly active nutrients and substances that like the reverse of a poison, run rapidly and purposefully throughout the bodily system, toning up the biochemistry and stimulating the body's infinitely complex mechanisms into protective action from all varieties of outside negative influences.

Bee Products: Honey, Royal Jelly, Propolis and Pollen

The amazing honey bee also produces a range of substances with most remarkable properties. Honey, royal jelly, pollen and propolis are the four substances that have been used in folk and traditional medicine around the world since long ago. Although I have seen no published reports on the effect of bee products on organisms exposed to radiation, their properties of strengthening, toning and increasing resistance to disease make them prime choices for use in an anti-radiation diet.

Propolis is bee-cement, secreted by bees as a binding

material for their hives. The least exploited by man of the bee products, this substance has antibiotic properties and is used in Sweden and Denmark to fight infections.

Royal Jelly contains practically every known life-supporting nutrient. It is secreted by young worker bees as the sole food for the queen. In fact, it is the content of the royal jelly which transforms a larva which would have otherwise grown up into a simple worker, into a large queen bee (not 'large green bee', as my typist would have had it!) capable of laying over 2000 eggs per day. It is used in innumerable beauty preparations and has a superb record in improving bodily oxygenation, stabilizing blood pressure, promoting speedy healing of tissues and, like ginseng, it increases the resistance to stress.

Pollen, the male reproductive germ cell of plants, is high in all the essential vitamins including the rarity, B_{12}, and contains many trace minerals, hormones and enzymes – all highly beneficial as human nutrients. Like royal jelly, it is widely used to increase endurance and well-being.

Honey itself contains about three-quarters natural sugars, plus many of the B vitamins, vitamin C and a goodly number of important minerals. It has been used in natural healing for aeons and carries an excellent reputation for conditions as diverse as kidney and liver dysfunction and arthritis. We use it, too, as an essential ingredient in a burn and wound formula that also contains wheatgerm oil (vitamin E) and fresh, homogenized, comfrey leaf. Using this formula, even major burns and wounds heal amazingly, without irritation or scarring. Honey is also a superb natural anti-microbial agent.

As with the ginseng, you need to be careful of the honey and other bee products you purchase. Most commercial honey is heated and strained which leaves it denatured and with many of its natural ingredients removed or destroyed. Royal jelly is best in its natural form, to be kept in a refrigerator and with pollen, too, try and determine which is the least processed.

The Macrobiotic Approach

On August 6th and 9th, 1945 the first nuclear weapons were used by mankind against themselves. As most people are aware, they were exploded above the Japanese cities of Hiroshima and Nagasaki causing destruction and agonizing death to hundreds of thousands of innocent people. Whatever the rights and wrongs, there is no doubt that the intense family squabble amongst the people of our planet had got wildly out of control.

At this time Dr Tatsuichiro Akizuki M.D. was director of the Department of Internal Medicine at St. Francis's Hospital, in Nagasaki. Dr. Akizuki was a follower of the dietary principles and lifestyle encompassed by the philosophy of macrobiotics.

In literal translation, *macro* is the Greek word for 'large' or 'great', while *bios* means life. The first recorded use of the term is found in the writings of Hippocrates, the father of modern medicine, meaning just that: healthy and long-lived. The term was later used by other classical writers, including Aristotle and Galen, where it came to mean a simple and healthy diet and lifestyle leading to an active old age.

These principles of health, by this or any other name, are intrinsic in nature, surfacing wherever people are in tune with themselves and the cosmos and coloured only by local idiom and circumstance. Like essential spiritual truths, they can be found in the writings of all cultures, of all ages.

In the latter part of the last century and the early years of the twentieth century, two Japanese, Dr Sagen Ishitsuka M.D. and Yukikazu Sakurazawa, cured themselves of serious illness by relinquishing the refined and processed foods then sweeping the 'civilized' world, including Japan, and reverting to their traditional diet including unrefined brown rice, grains, miso soup and sea vegetables.

Rediscovering for themselves the power of the natural, they integrated this approach with both traditional Oriental and Ayurvedic medicine, as well as the natural principles within Western medicine and science. When Sakurazawa moved to Paris, in the 1920's, he called his philosophy *macrobiotics* and adopted the pen name by which he is more popularly known – George Ohsawa.

Macrobiotic principles understand the basic duality or polarity of nature. The Chinese call this the *Yin* (negative) and the *Yang* (positive). By balancing the Yin and Yang in all aspects of one's life, health, well-being and harmony are the natural result.

Dr Akizuki of the Nagasaki hospital of St. Francis was a student of Sakurazawa. The inmates of his hospital had been fed a balanced diet, based on macrobiotic principles, including miso, brown rice and sea vegetables. And not one of the 3000 inmates died, whilst 8000 died in the immediately surrounding area. (Miso is a concentrate prepared from soya beans, cereals and sea salt. It can be purchased at health food shops and can be used in the preparation of soups, especially in conjunction with sea vegetables.)

The macrobiotic diet is high in minerals and nutrients, but above all, when understood correctly, it is a *balanced* diet, in the deeper meaning of the term. Dr Akizuki, realizing that he, his staff and patients were indescribably better off than the multitude of sufferers around them, took their diet as the main source of their protection and helped innumerable people by feeding them this simple diet.

A few scientists, coming to hear in later years of this almost miraculous event have attempted to identify the 'active ingredients' in this diet. One should not, however, miss the point inherent in the principles of balance and harmony, necessary for health and well-being at any level – mental, emotional, subtle, sub-atomic, molecular, physiological or anatomical – that the *whole* diet is important, not just the 'active ingredient'. Scientists have, however, discovered some interesting facts of which we can take specific advantage.

In Canada, Dr Y. Tanaka and his colleagues, in 1968, published their research findings in the Canadian Medical Association Journal. Sodium alginate, an active principle in algin, was extracted from kelp and other brown sea-weeds and fed to laboratory rats in conjunction with strontium 90 and calcium, when it was found that the elimination of the strontium isotope from the bone, measured in the femur (upper leg) was as much as 80%. Sodium alginate, a polysaccharide, appears to selectively bind the radioactive strontium and help in its elimination. It is this ability of certain natural nutrients to selectively absorb toxic materials from the body and to aid in their elimination that underlies the functioning of the heavy metal purifiers mentioned above. It is also a further good reason why kelp, which contains both iodine and sodium alginate, is a better source of protection against radiation than pure iodine.

The tendency of the modern 'scientific' mind to zero in on one part of a whole, to the exclusion of the whole, represents a fundamental flaw in understanding natural principles. As human beings, we are by nature ignorant of the vastly complex interchanges of energy around us. We know this, yet very few will admit it to themselves and understand its deeper implications.

Similarly, Japanese scientists in 1970, at the Japanese National Cancer Centre Research Institute, reported that polysaccharides prepared from a variety of natural sources, including shiitake mushrooms, readily available on the streets of Tokyo, significantly inhibited the growth of induced tumours in laboratory mice. Other polysaccharides, especially lentinan from the edible mushroom, *Lentinus edodes*, were also found to be highly effective. And mushrooms are frequently used in the macrobiotic diet.

Then again, I. Yamamoto and his colleagues reported in 1974 in the *Japanese Journal of Experimental Medicine* that several varieties of mojaban and kombu, common sea vegetables in Asia and used traditionally in Chinese medicine as a decoction for cancer, inhibited the growth of implanted tumours in laboratory mice by as much as 89 to 95 per cent. The tumours were not only stabilized but in more than fifty per cent of cases, they regressed. Yamamoto has also been conducting trials on mice with leukaemia, with similar encouraging results.

In 1981, the National Cancer Centre of Japan published the results of a ten-year study, revealing that those who ate miso soup were one third less prone to stomach cancer than those who did not. Miso was also shown to be effective in the prevention of liver and heart disease. This study was inspired by studies of victims of the Japanese atomic explosions.

And so the story continues. *Rutin*, as found in the cereal buckwheat, has also been shown clinically to have protective properties against the effect of radiation, though it has been known to ancient medicine in the Far East for many ages to have wonderful protective and curative properties. So it can hardly be claimed as a new discovery. Buckwheat, is also used in the macrobiotic diet.

In general, therefore, it appears that the macrobiotic diet contains many substances that are specific in their inhibition of cancer either from radiation or other causes. Miso and sea vegetables are in common use in Japan and it is natural for their scientists to have concentrated research on these substances, in order to identify some of the active principles. But let it never be thought that a wonder-cure drug can be found in this way. The cure lay in the balanced diet that contained the nutrients necessary to fight off the ill effects of radiation. Only some of these nutrients and just a small part of the biochemical network in which they are involved have been identified.

Similarly, in our present times, it is those living healthy lifestyles who are less prone to cancers or any other form of degenerative disease brought about by imbalance in our modern circumstances. Junk food and pollutants of all kinds should carry a government health warning! There is no need for them to be in use.

Miscellaneous Special Nutrients

We have also heard of a number of other nutrients and foods that have been found of value in counteracting the effect of radiation. Unfortunately, we have been unable to trace the source of the research, but since so many natural substances have been found to possess rejuvenating, strengthening, anti-cancer and anti-radiation properties, they most probably have authentic research behind them. Two of these, which are certainly good foods in their own right are:

1. **Pectin**, especially as found in sunflower seeds, which helps reduce the absorption of radioactive materials from the alimentary canal.

2. **Lecithin** is said to reduce the effect of radiation when fed to laboratory animals. The name comes from the Greek which means egg yolk and it is also found in milk, soya beans and other products, as well as being manufactured within the body itself. Lecithin is an important source of choline – an essential precursor in the formation of the

neurotransmitter, acetyl choline, which facilitates transmission of nerve signals at their junctions or synapses. Lecithin is generally important for the functioning of a healthy brain and nervous system and it therefore makes an excellent 'brain food' or tonic for the nervous system.

Exercise

How can exercise reduce the effects of radiation? Quite generally, of course, anything that strengthens your system will be of value and exercise will do just that, but quite specifically certain kinds of exercise, notably jumping and exercising on a rebound unit or aerobic bouncer (a kind of firm, mini-trampoline), places each cell under the combined stresses of gravity, acceleration and deceleration and is a wonderful stimulator of the lymphatic system. Many of the lymph vessels pass between the muscles and rely on their regular use for movement of lymph fluid. Aerobic rebounding especially, as well as other forms of exercise, stimulates the cells to dump their toxins into the lymph from where it is ultimately excreted or eliminated through the skin, bowels or the kidneys.

Aerobic forms of exercise, that is, those forms that result in a greater conveyance of oxygen to the tissues than others, will clearly aid in the energy-releasing oxidation-reduction sequences within the body, also deactivating toxins, radicals and waste products for their later expulsion from the body through the normal eliminative channels.

So if you don't take regular exercise, now is a good time to start and with a bouncer you can also exercise indoors in your normal clothes. They are very good for people who don't really like taking exercise, but feel that they should, as well as being used by fitness enthusiasts and athletes.

Mental and Emotional Attitudes

Our mind and thoughts directly affect our biochemistry and physical health through the outworking of subtle energies and their crystallization as electromagnetic, sub-atomic, atomic and molecular energy patterns. This is very clear from observations of oneself and others. It has obvious aspects – if you get a fright for example, then adrenaline and its associated complex of biochemical reactions are put into action immediately. The information is transformed from the outside cause of the fright, through our sense organs, into neural impulses in the brain, into our emotions and mind and back into our nervous and hormonal system, stimulating the adrenal gland into the production of adrenaline, which further prepares the body for action.

If you think that this process does not require the influence of mind and emotion then try frightening a dead person or someone who is so fast asleep or unconscious that he is unaware of the source of fright! Consciousness and higher energies are definitely required.

A strong, positive, loving, understanding and balanced outlook on life with emotions under (reasonable) control will lead to less ill-health and less susceptibility to environmental pollution of all kinds. Worrying and negative attitudes will attract disharmonized biochemical and physiological energy patterns of dis-ease. Many times, people unconsiously *want* to be ill. It is their way of existing and solving the problems of how to relate to other people and outer reality.

Books could be written on this subject, as indeed they have been, but let me say briefly that any harmonizing influences on your psychology will have positive benefits on your physical health and the way you feel. Meditation is the first step, if you can manage it. Then, hatha yoga or ta'i ch'i (special physical exercises with remarkable subtle effects) can be very helpful in bringing you into both inner and biological balance.

You can also try changing the trend of negative thoughts by making strong positive affirmations to yourself. If you really feel the need you can take good psychological counselling – we all need good advice at critical times in our life.

We need to develop therefore, a balanced approach to life. This, in itself, will create health and harmony.

A Cleansing and Drawing Programme

Spa waters have been known from time immemorial to have health giving properties. Naturopathic doctors attribute this property to their ability to draw toxic materials out of the body through the skin, as well as to other aspects of the water's mineral content.

It is not always appreciated that the skin is one of the major eliminative channels of the body and its healthy functioning is essential to your vitality and well-being.

Certain minerals, when dissolved in hot water which opens up the pores, have the ability to attract toxins, including heavy metals, from the body and the following simple programme is used by naturopaths in the absence of mineral baths and saunas.

Firstly, you dissolve two cups of Epsom salts (*Magnesium Sulphate*) in a bath of hot water and then allow yourself to soak in it for say ten or fifteen minutes. Then, rub yourself all over with a paste of sodium bicarbonate. This cleans the pores and the skin. Then wash off the paste – a shower is useful if you have one – and repeat the Epsom salts bath. If you think that this is something that granny must have dreamt up, then just think: you could be a grandparent yourself one day, if you're not already. Traditional natural medicine contains many such gems. It is only human stupidity that makes us think that people a few hundred years ago didn't know anything, but somehow we do. Do you not think that people in a hundred or a thousand years time will think the same of us? But then, maybe they would be right.

This treatment helps to cleanse the skin very thoroughly, also drawing out toxic materials including radioactive substances, from within the body.

Homoeopathy and Radiation

Most people have heard of homoeopathy and probably know that the Queen and some members of the Royal Family use homoeopathic remedies. This has given an aura of respectability to what is to most people a little understood subject. Homoeopathy is also one of the few alternative therapies available on the NHS (National Health Service), through general practitioners who also practise homoeopathy.

Homoeopathy uses the subtle essence or vibration of its materia medica to treat problems of ill-health, usually treating like with like in order to stimulate the body's natural defences at the subtle level and without toxic side-effects.

It is a complex science and as with all wholistic medicine, the patient is treated as a whole, so it is not so easy to specify which remedies are suitable for protection against radiation. It depends, too, on factors within the patient themselves. There are, however, two specific remedies which may be beneficial against radiation in homoeopathic potency, these being thorium nitrate and radium bromide. If you are interested in using these remedies, we would advise you to seek a qualified homoeopath. There are also other homoeopathic remedies for strengthening and toning one's energy, as well as the biochemic tissue salts, but professional advice is always best since each case requires an individual prescription.

Bach Flower Remedies

Similar in some respects to homoeopathic remedies are the Bach Flower Remedies. Dr Edward Bach was a qualified medical doctor and virologist who moved into homoeopathy as a more wholistic approach to a patient, but subsequently discovered that certain plant and tree flowers contained a subtle energy essence that could be used to treat the personality of the patient. Since – observed Bach – illness always starts at the mental-emotional energy pattern level, it can also be treated from this higher level.

Dr Bach believed in simplicity and those who use his remedies can vouch for their efficacy, though their concept would probably make the hairs curl on the knees of the British Medical Association! However, Dr Aubrey Westlake BA, MB, B Chir, MRCS LRCP is a user of Dr Bach's remedies and many years ago he formulated a composite remedy to strengthen the body's energy system against the effects of radiation. The formula is as follows:

Cherry Plum: For the fear of being overstrained and of reason giving way.

Gentian: For the uncertainty.

Star of Bethlehem: For distress and shock, this remedy brings comfort.

Rock Rose: The remedy for emergency, for fear,
                      this remedy brings calmness.

Vine: To give support to those who can be
                      leaders. Aids self-reliance.

Walnut: To give protection from outside
                      influences.

Wild Oat: For indecision and being unsure
                      what course of action to take.

Dr Bach's short and simple writings are full of compassion and deep understanding and I have paraphrased the relevant passages from his book, *The Twelve Healers and Other Remedies*.

The formula is made up as follows: put two drops of each stock remedy into a solution of 3.5 grams of sea salt (Tidman's is said to be the purest) in 100ml of pure spring water. Four drops of this remedy should be taken four times a day or whenever the need is felt. It will help combat the effect not only of radiation, but also of TV's, computer displays, radiation therapy and X-ray's.

Subtle Energy Balancing – Pulsors®

Both homoeopathic and Bach remedies work directly on the biophysical or subtle energy blueprint of the body. If you are not familiar with this way of thinking, then you'll probably be doubting their efficacy, but let me assure you that these remedies do work. Acupuncture, too, and many other forms of therapy also work in part or wholly on the subtle energy levels and can be used to strengthen your resistance to all illness and pollution, including radiation.

One such method which seems to draw together modern physics and ancient healing wisdom is the creation of Dr George Yao of California, a materials scientist and physical chemist who turned his interests to naturopathy and wholistic healing. The result has been a unique device called a Pulsor, also known as a bio-crystal resonator.

Pulsor® is a registered trademark of Yao International.

Pulsors have piezo-electric properties and use millions of specially processed micro-crystals to resonate with and therefore amplify the body's natural subtle energy field, thereby strengthening one's resistance to external influences, including not only radiation, but also TV's, computer terminals, electrical cabling, negative atmospheres and influences and subtle energy fields of all kinds.

The active crystalline material is encased within plastic or ceramic discs about one and a half inches in diameter or within natural stone pendants and they are worn upon the body. I have personally used these Pulsors for some time and have found them highly energizing in a very natural way. We also use them in treatment, because there are, in fact, a number of different 'frequencies' available which can be used for tuning and harmonizing the body's energy system. They are not an easy concept to grasp at first sight, but they do very definitely work.

In Conclusion

And so we reach the end of this little book that I wish there had been no occasion to write. But perhaps it will be a lead-in to exciting avenues of thought and research and out of the negative, can be drawn some positive advantage. I am non-political in my views. I simply feel myself to be a member of a vast family and like all families the members seem to have their differences and problems. So let the leaders of our various universal sub-families do their duty by their people and find solutions to some very obvious problems just as soon as they can, before it is too late.

Epilogue

I have written this book specifically on radiation and what to do about it, because the subject is topical. But actually, the chapter on natural protection from radiation, although containing many specifics for radiation, can be taken as a model for combatting the many forms of pollution that surround us.

The latest method of disturbing the natural balance in our food and therefore our bodies, is by irradiating it with intense X-rays or gamma rays in order to kill bacteria and make it last longer. This is not for the benefit of the consumer, of course, but for the increased profit of the suppliers, because the food will stay looking fresh for longer periods. Food irradiation will have the following effects:

1. The molecular structure will be denatured, as we have described in these pages, altering its food value and nutritional qualities. This denaturing will be different from that to which the human body has ever before been subjected. Certain of the new or damaged molecules are likely to be harmful in the long term. Very little, if any, biochemical research has actually been done on this new biochemistry. Experimentation has been performed on laboratory animals over just a few years with no significant decrease in their longevity. But unfortunately, the experimenters were unable to determine how the animals *felt* on their new irradiated diet or whether they were as full of energy as previously. It is sheer egotism and ignorance to feel that we know so much about the biochemical pathways in our nutrition and bodies that we can change them around at random by introducing new substances. No-one would ever consider tinkering with the compon-

ents in a vast and complex computing system and expect to get away without modifying its functioning. It will immediately behave differently. The body is an infinitely more complex and interwoven system with a high level of adaptability, and feeding it with new and unknown molecules will definitely alter its functioning. It can go on living under intolerable circumstances, but the quality of life is definitely affected and probably its longevity.

2. There is great value in consuming *live* fruits and vegetables. Irradiation will kill fresh produce, even if it goes on having the external appearance of being alive. This is considered advantageous by produce suppliers because, for example, potatoes do not sprout (because they are dead). But there is a subtle life energy in living fruits and vegetables that is essential to true vitality and vibrant health. This will be missing from irradiated foods.

3. There are micro-organisms that we ingest with our food which are essential to our health – bacteria in the intestines, for example. Irradiation will kill them, causing problems similar to some of the side-effects of antibiotics which also kill off these symbiotic bacteria, creating digestive and therefore other problems. There are also magnetically sensitive bacteria living symbiotically in our blood. The full story of their function is not understood, but one of their jobs is known to be that of helping with the formation of blood clots to stem bleeding from cuts and wounds. There is also the strong possibility that not all bacteria and viruses will be destroyed by the proposed irradiation, resulting in mutated forms carrying on a modified and potentially dangerous or health-reducing activity within our bodies.

4. Irradiation will leave a small, induced radioactivity (i.e. unstable atoms) in food stuffs. This is *considered* to be harmless, though I do not believe that such a conclusion can be genuinely arrived at. It is a matter of opinion,

not proven fact. People vary so much in their sensitivities to radiation and pollution, from medical as well as environmental sources, that it is impossible to make such sweeping statements. And if background radiation is supposed to be responsible for 2000 cancer cases per year in Great Britain, then NO level of radiation can be considered safe.

Actually, it is background radiation that is thought to be responsible for the spontaneous mutations that allow species to evolve. Most of these mutations are negative, biologically speaking, and result, ultimately, in the demise of the creature and its progeny. Only a very few are considered, by chance, to be just the right thing at the right time, resulting in a positive evolutionary step. So even within the current 'scientific' framework, the facts run counter to each other.

5. The subtle energy harmonies of the food will be disturbed, reflecting as similar disharmonies in those who eat it.

Man is, quite rapidly by historical perspective, destroying his biological strength. And this at a time when he should be using his new-found technology to increase his health, strength, happiness, well-being and even leisure. Every civilization has ultimately passed away or shifted direction. Often their strengths have become their weaknesses and caused their demise. There are always ways to justify selfish motives and to keep doing what we want to do despite the obvious consequences. Our technologically-based civilization is destroying itself through rape of the environment and the pollution of the life-supporting elements and nutrients that constitute the source of our physical life. Degenerative diseases already account for the vast majority of deaths. We may have eliminated smallpox and almost eliminated bubonic plague, but we have substituted our own killers in their place. Can we really say that we are better off? We should take advantage of our increased (though still small) knowledge of biochemistry, physiology and nutrition to lead healthier lives, not squander our knowledge by polluting our environment and irreversibly denaturing our foods.

But there are signs that the tide is definitely turning. People are becoming more aware; they are not so easily duped by clever advertising, by party politics and by the misuse of statistics. Let us hope it is not too late to return our planet to being a natural place in which to live, whilst still taking full advantage of our abilities with technology.

Bibliography and Further Reading

Diet, Nutrition and Health

Ageless Ageing, Leslie Kenton; Century, 1985.
Antitumour Effect of Seaweeds, I. Yamamoto et al; Japanese Journal of Experimental Medicine, 44:543 – 546.
The Cancer Prevention Diet, Michio Kushi with Alex Jack; Thorsons, 1984.
Chemistry of Man, Dr. Bernard Jensen; Jensen, 1983.
Documentary of A-Bombed Nagasaki, Dr. T. Akizuki, M.D., Nagasaki Printing Co, 1977.
Food Healing For Man, Dr. Bernard Jensen; Jensen, 1983.
Fractionation and Purification of the Polysaccharides with Marked Anti-tumour Activity, Especially Lentinan from Lentinus edodes (Berk.) Sing. (An edible Mushroom), G. Chihara et al; Cancer Research 30:2776-81
Glowing Health Through Diet and Posture, D. & J. Lawson-Wood; Health Science Press, 1973.
Miracle Cure – Organic Germanium, Kazuhiko Asai, Ph. D.; Japan Publications, 1980.
Report from Japan H. Ohmori; A Nutritional Approach to Cancer, East West Foundation, Boston, 1977 pp.28–32.
The Twelve Healers and Other Remedies, Dr E. Bach; C.W. Daniel, 1983.

Herbalism

The Book of Ginseng, Sarah Harriman; Pyramid Books, 1975.
Chinese Tonic Herbs, Ron Teeguarden; Japanese Publications, 1985.
The Complete Book of Ginseng, Richard Heffern; Celestial Arts, 1976.
Energy Guide, East Earth Herbs, 1983.

Herbs of Grace, Farida Davidson; Herbs of Grace, 1986.

The Tao of Medicine – Ginseng, Oriental Remedies and the Pharmacology of Harmony, Stephan Fulder; Destiny Books, 1980.

The Way of Herbs, Michael Tierra; Washington Square Press, 1980.

Nuclear and Electromagnetic Radiation

The Cycles of Heaven, Guy Lyon Playfair and Scott Hill; Souvenir, 1978.

Electromagnetic Fields and Life, A.S. Presman; Plenum, 1970.

The Menace of Electric Smog, Lowell Ponte; Readers Digest, U.S.A., January 1980.

Models for the Prediction of Doses from the Ingestion of Terrestrial Foods, Nair, Grogan, Miniski & Bell, Undated scientific paper.

New Scientist Articles, May 8th, 15th and 22nd 1986. Wilkie, Milne, Taylor, Kingman, Mason.

Pollution Begins at Home, Robert Matthews; New Scientist, December 5th, 1985.

Radiation – How Safe Is 'Safe', BBC TV Panorama, May 12th 1986.

Studies on Inhibition of Intestinal Absorbtion of Radio-Active Strontium, Y. Tanaka et al; Canadian Medical Journal 99:169-75

Pollution Issues

A Harmony of Science and Nature, Ways of Staying Healthy in a Modern World, John and Farida Davidson; Wholistic Research Company, 1986.

Subtle Energy

Health Building, The Conscious Art of Living Well, Dr Randolph Stone; CRCS, 1985.

Pulsor Seminars, Dr George Yao; Cambridge, October 1984 & April 1986.

Radionics and The Subtle Anatomy of Man, David Tansley; C.W. Daniel, 1972.

The Raiment of Light, David Tansley; Routledge and Kegan Paul, 1984.

Subtle Energy, John Davidson M.A. Cantab; C.W. Daniel, 1986.

Further Scientific Papers by Subject

1. Measurement of very small magnetic fields associated with brain waves.
   M. Reite and J. Zimmerman; Annual Review of Biophysics and Bioengineering, 1978, 7, 167–188.

2. Review of creatures able to detect the earth's magnetic field.
   R.B. Frankel; Annual Review of Bioengineering, 1984, 13, 85–103.

3. Incidence of Leukaemia amongst amateur radio operators in U.S.A.
   S. Milham; Lancet, 1982, i, 246.

4. Incidence of Leukaemia amongst electrical workers in New Zealand.
   N.E. Pearce, R.A. Shepherd, J.K. Howard, J. Fraser, B.M. Lilley, Lancet, 1985, i, 811–812.

5. Incidence of Leukaemia in homes adjacent to electricity power lines.
   J.P. Fulton, S. Cobb, L. Preble, L. Leone, E. Forman; American Journal of Epidemiology, 111, 292–296.
   N. Wertheimer, E. Leeper; American Journal of Epidemiology, 1979, 109, 273–284.
   N. Wertheimer, E. Leeper; International Journal of Epidemiology, 1982, 11, 345–355.
   L. Tomenius, L. Hellstrom, B. Enander; International Symposium on Occupational Health and Safety in Mining and Tunnelling, 1982, Prague.

Further Information

Many of the items mentioned in this book can be obtained from:

WHOLISTIC RESEARCH COMPANY
Bright Haven, Robin's Lane,
Lolworth, Cambridge CB3 8HH, England.
Telephone: Craft's Hill (0954) 81074

Please send £1.95 (£4 if overseas), for their full catalogue and product details, including the book, *A Harmony Of Science & Nature – Ways Of Staying Healthy In A Modern World* by John & Farida Davidson. This book is normally £3.95 and is more or less essential for understanding the thinking behind their products.